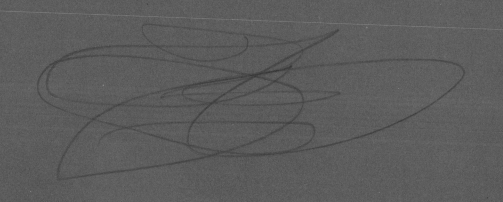

Edith Fowke SALLY GO

300 SONGS, RHYMES AND GAMES OF CANADIAN CHILDREN

ROUND THE SUN

McCLELLAND AND STEWART LIMITED   TORONTO / MONTREAL

Collected and edited by Edith Fowke
Musical arrangements by Keith MacMillan
Illustrated by Carlos Marchiori

This volume was designed by
Frank Newfeld and Don Fernley

PRINTED AND BOUND IN ITALY

CONTENTS

Introduction

Today most traditional folklore is fast dying out because the people who used to sing songs and tell stories for their own amusement are now listening to records or watching television. But children's lore is still as much alive as it ever was. You can go into any playground and hear youngsters chanting age-old rhymes as they twirl their skipping ropes or bounce their balls.

These rhymes do not come to children through their parents or teachers: they pick them up from other children, who in their turn learned them from the children before them. This constant re-transmission solely within the child world is doubly remarkable when you remember that such rhymes are current only in the six-to-eleven age group, so there is a complete turn-over every five years, contrasted with adult lore which may be passed on at any time throughout a long life.

Most of the children's rhymes have roots in the distant past, but they are constantly being reshaped as they pass from one child generation to the next, a process that gives them their unique flavour. If you hear a group of youngsters chanting some verses that sound as though they had been made up on the spot, the chances are that they can be matched by similar ones dating back several generations – or several centuries.

This selection of children's lore includes singing games, rhymes used for skipping, ball bouncing, and clapping, formulas for counting out, taunts and teases, nonsense verses, parodies, and snatches of old songs. They take many forms and cover a multitude of subjects, but taken together they form the folk poetry of childhood. They show the child's natural instinct for rhythm, his love of rhyme, his delight in playing with words, and his flights of fancy.

The verses reflect his many changing moods for they are in turn romantic, realistic, imaginative, prosaic, sentimental, and saucy. One minute they chant of a girl in a golden city; the next they tell of a backyard fight. Characters from history, comic strips, fairy tales, and movies are recruited as actors, and familiar verses and popular songs are adapted to new uses.

All these rhymes and games have been current in North America within the present century. Most of them were collected from children between the ages of five and eleven within the last ten years; the rest came from adults who remembered them from their own childhoods.

Most children's rhymes ignore national boundaries: you can hear very similar lines echoing through the streets of London, Edinburgh, Dublin, Sydney, New York, or Toronto. But a few do take on local colour, and certain ones seem more popular in some areas than in others. Even though many of these rhymes turn up in similar books from the British Isles or the United States, the collection as a whole is definitely Canadian because every item in it has been chanted by Canadian children. Some old rhymes have acquired Canadian references, and a few that are popular in our country have not yet spread beyond its borders. Anyone interested in tracing the history of the items in this collection will find references to other sources at the end of the book.

In compiling the games, I concentrated on those that use songs or rhymes, leaving out the many other traditional games that depend on action or a ritual that does not fall into the rhyming pattern. In selecting rhymes, I favoured those used for activities

of all English-speaking children, choosing instead the rhymes that originated with children rather than with adults. A few of the rhymes probably did come from adults originally, and some of the songs were learned in summer camps, but all those given here have been adopted and passed on by children.

I am grateful to all the children who chanted these rhymes for me, and to the adults who shared their memories of their youth. In particular I wish to thank Miss Alice Kane, Mrs. Isabel Smaller, Mrs. Nellie Webb, Mrs. Marion Robertson, Mrs. Kate Hansen, Harry Walker, Philip J. Thomas, and Barry Hall, who generously allowed me to use some of the rhymes they had collected from children in their areas, thus making this book more representative of the lore of children everywhere.

I am also very grateful to Keith MacMillan who patiently and skilfully transcribed the melodies from assorted tapes. He also provided guitar chords for all the melodies, and piano accompaniments for those that lend themselves to harmonization.

I hope that children will enjoy finding some rhymes here that they do not know, that parents will enjoy learning what their children chant when they are outside playing, and that teachers will find some of the songs and games useful in their classrooms.

EDITH FOWKE

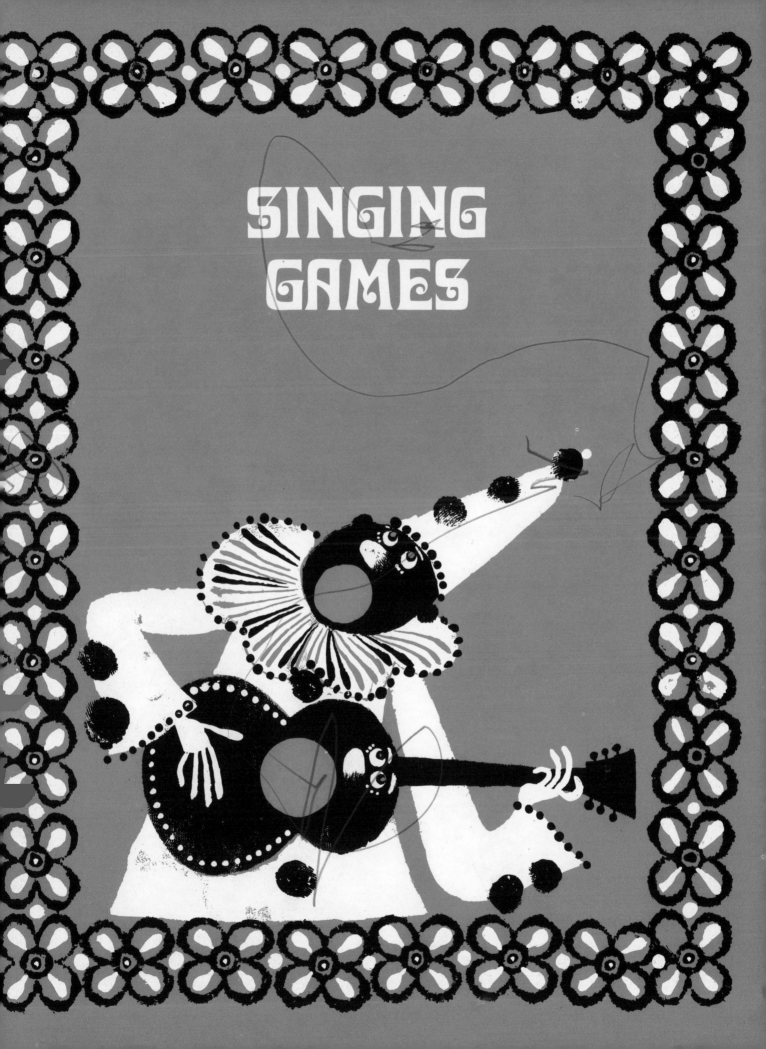

RING GAMES

1 *Sally go round the sun*

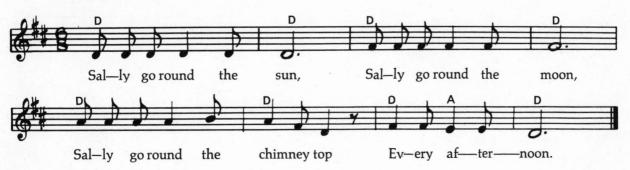

Sal—ly go round the sun, Sal—ly go round the moon, Sal—ly go round the chimney top Ev—ery af—ter——noon.

2 *Ring around a rosy*

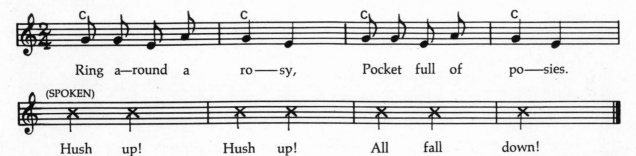

Ring a—round a ro——sy, Pocket full of po—sies.

(SPOKEN)

Hush up! Hush up! All fall down!

3 *I wrote a letter to my love*

I wrote a let—ter to my love And on the way I dropped it. A lit—tle dog—gie picked it up And put it in his pock——et. And he won't bite you, and he won't bite you, but he will bite *you!*

4 _Rig-a-jig-jig_

As I was walk—ing down the street, Down the street, down the street, A

pret——ty boy I chanced to meet, Hi——ho! Hi—ho! Hi——ho!

Rig-a-jig-jig and a——way we go, And a——way we go, and a——way we go!

Rig-a-jig-jig and a——way we go, Hi——ho! Hi—ho! Hi——ho!

5 The farmer in the dell

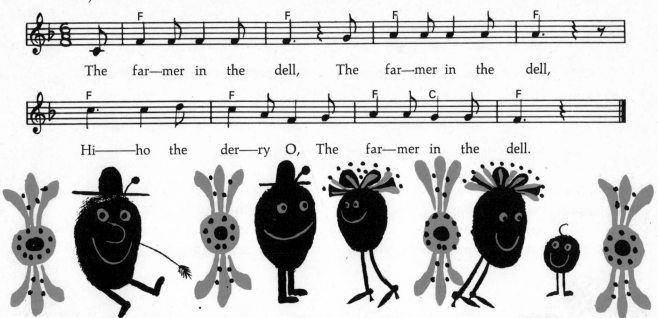

The far—mer in the dell, The far—mer in the dell,

Hi——ho the der—ry O, The far—mer in the dell.

The farmer in the dell,
The farmer in the dell,
Hi ho the derry O,
The farmer in the dell.

The farmer takes the wife,
The farmer takes the wife,
Hi ho the derry O,
The farmer takes the wife.

The wife takes the child,
The wife takes the child,
Hi ho the derry O,
The wife takes the child.

The child takes the nurse,
The child takes the nurse,
Hi ho the derry O,
The child takes the nurse.

The nurse takes the dog,
The nurse takes the dog,
Hi ho the derry O,
The nurse takes the dog.

The dog takes the cat,
The dog takes the cat,
Hi ho the derry O,
The dog takes the cat.

 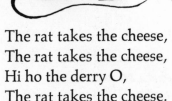  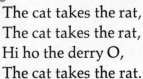

The cat takes the rat,
The cat takes the rat,
Hi ho the derry O,
The cat takes the rat.

The rat takes the cheese,
The rat takes the cheese,
Hi ho the derry O,
The rat takes the cheese.

We all take a bite,
We all take a bite,
Hi ho the derry O,
We all take a bite.

6 Oats, peas, beans, and barley grow

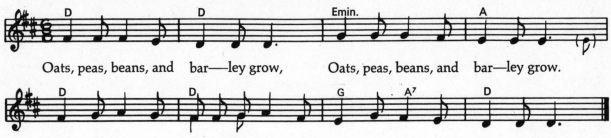

Oats, peas, beans, and bar—ley grow, Oats, peas, beans, and bar—ley grow.

You or I or no—bo—dy knows How oats, peas, beans, and bar—ley grow.

Oats, peas, beans, and barley grow,
Oats, peas, beans, and barley grow.
You or I or nobody knows
How oats, peas, beans, and barley grow.

Thus the farmer sows his seed,
Thus the farmer sows his seed.
He stamps his foot and claps his hands
And turns around to view his land.

Waiting for a partner,
Waiting for a partner,
Open the ring and take her in,
And kiss her when you get her in.

7 Punchinello

Look who is here, Pun—chin——el—lo, fun—ny fel—low.

Look who is here, Pun—chin——el—lo, fun—ny boy.

Look who is here,
Punchinello, funny fellow.
Look who is here,
Punchinello, funny boy.

What can you do,
Punchinello, funny fellow?
What can you do,
Punchinello, funny boy?

We can do it too,
Punchinello, funny fellow.
We can do it too,
Punchinello, funny boy.

8 *The mulberry bush*

Here we go round the mulber-ry bush, Mulber-ry bush, mulber-ry bush.

Here we go round the mulber-ry bush So ear——ly in the morn——ing.

REFRAIN:
Here we go round the mulberry bush,
Mulberry bush, mulberry bush.
Here we go round the mulberry bush
So early in the morning.

This is the way we wash our clothes,
Wash our clothes, wash our clothes.
This is the way we wash our clothes
So early Monday morning.

This is the way we iron our clothes,
Iron our clothes, iron our clothes.
This is the way we iron our clothes
So early Tuesday morning.

This is the way we mend our clothes,
Mend our clothes, mend our clothes.
This is the way we mend our clothes
So early Wednesday morning.

This is the way we sweep our floors,
Sweep our floors, sweep our floors.
This is the way we sweep our floors
So early Thursday morning.

This is the way we scrub our floors,
Scrub our floors, scrub our floors.
This is the way we scrub our floors
So early Friday morning.

This is the way we bake our bread,
Bake our bread, bake our bread.
This is the way we bake our bread
So early Saturday morning.

This is the way we go to church,
Go to church, go to church.
This is the way we go to church
So early Sunday morning.

9 Monkey see and monkey do

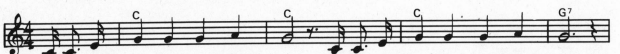

The monkey stamp, stamp, stamps his feet. The monkey stamp, stamp, stamps his feet.

Mon—key see and mon—key do, The mon—key does the same as you.

The monkey stamp, stamp, stamps his feet.
The monkey stamp, stamp, stamps his feet.
Monkey see and monkey do,
The monkey does the same as you.

The monkey clap, clap, claps his hands.
The monkey clap, clap, claps his hands.
Monkey see and monkey do,
The monkey does the same as you.

When you make a funny face, the monkey makes a funny face.
When you make a funny face, the monkey makes a funny face.
Monkey see and monkey do,
The monkey does the same as you.

When you turn yourself around, the monkey turns himself around.
When you turn yourself around, the monkey turns himself around.
Monkey see and monkey do,
The monkey does the same as you.

10 Round the mountain

Here we go round the moun—tain, two by two. Here we go round the mountain,

two by two. Here we go round the moun—tain, two by two:

Rise,—— su—gar,—— rise!

Here we go round the mountain, two by two.
Here we go round the mountain, two by two.
Here we go round the mountain, two by two:
Rise, sugar, rise!

Show your pretty motion, two by two.
Show your pretty motion, two by two.
Show your pretty motion, two by two:
Rise, sugar, rise!

11 Looby loo

Here we go loo——by loo,   Here we go loo——by   light.

Here we go loo——by   loo   All on a Sat—ur—day   night.   You

Here we go looby loo,
Here we go looby light.
Here we go looby loo
All on a Saturday night.

    You put your left hand in,
    You put your left hand out,
    You shake it a little, a little, a little,
    And turn yourself about.

Here we go looby loo,
Here we go looby light.
Here we go looby loo
All on a Saturday night.

    You put your right hand in,
    You put your right hand out,
    You shake it a little, a little, a little,
    And turn yourself about.

Repeat for "your left leg,"
"your right leg," and "your whole self."

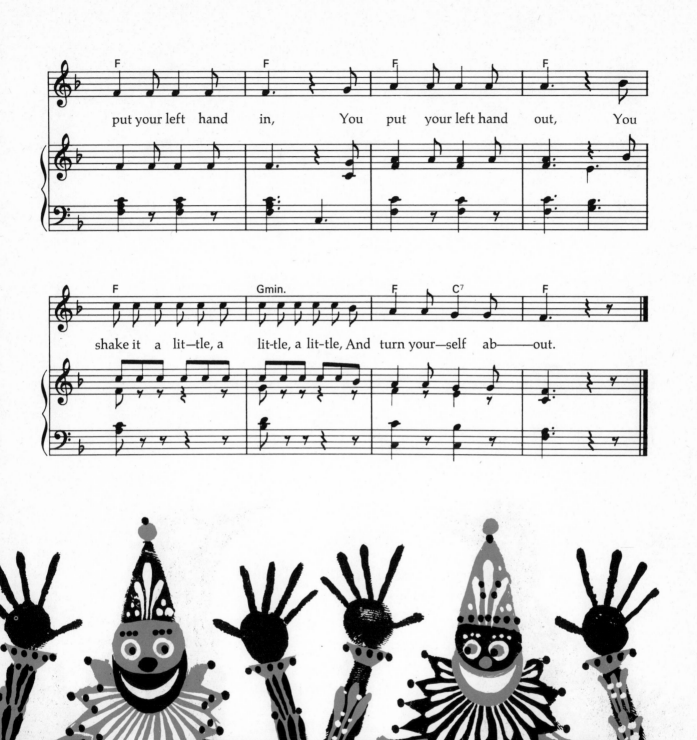

put your left hand in, You put your left hand out, You shake it a lit—tle, a lit-tle, a lit-tle, And turn your—self ab——out.

12 Here stands a red bird

Here stands a red bird, tra la la la la.
Here stands a red bird, tra la la la la.
Rice, sugar, and tea!

Let me see a motion, tra la la la la.
Let me see a motion, tra la la la la.
Rice, sugar, and tea!

Very pretty motion, tra la la la la.
Very pretty motion, tra la la la la.
Rice, sugar, and tea!

Get yourself a partner, tra la la la la.
Get yourself a partner, tra la la la la.
Rice, sugar and tea!

13 *Did you ever see a lassie?*

14 *When I was a baby*

When I was a baby, a baby, a baby,
When I was a baby, one, two, three:
Goo, goo, this-a-way, goo, goo, that-a-way,
Goo, goo, this-a-way, goo, goo, one, two, three.

When I was a bad girl, a bad girl, a bad girl,
When I was a bad girl, one, two, three:
No, no, this-a-way, no, no, that-away,
No, no, this-a-way, no, no, one, two, three.

When I was a teen-ager, teen-ager, teen-ager,
When I was a teen-ager, one, two, three:
Gab, gab, this-a-way, gab, gab, that-a-way,
Gab, gab, this-a-way, gab, gab, one, two, three.

When I had a boy friend, a boy friend, a boy friend,
When I had a boy friend, one, two, three:
Kiss, kiss, this-a-way, kiss, kiss, that-a-way,
Kiss, kiss, this-a-way, one, two, three.

15 *In and out the window*

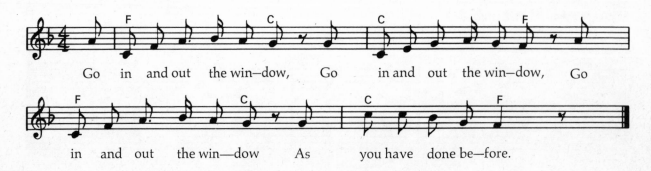

When I was engaged, engaged, engaged,
When I was engaged, one, two, three:
Ring, ring, this-a-way, ring, ring, that-a-way,
Ring, ring, this-a-way, one, two, three.

When I had my first child, my first child, my first child,
When I had my first child, one, two, three:
Rock, rock, this-a-way, rock, rock, that-a-way,
Rock, rock, this-a-way, one, two, three.

When I had my eighth child, my eighth child, my eighth child,
When I had my eighth child, one, two, three:
Shoo, shoo, this-a-way, shoo, shoo, that-a-way,
Shoo, shoo, this-a-way, one, two, three.

When my husband died, husband died, husband died,
When my husband died, one, two, three:
Rah, rah, this-a-way, rah, rah, that-a-way,
Rah, rah, this-a-way, one, two, three.

When my children died, children died, children died,
When my children died, one, two, three:
Sob, sob, this-a-way, sob, sob, that-a-way,
Sob, sob, this-a-way, one, two, three.
When I was dying, dying, dying,
When I was dying, one, two, THREE.

Go in and out the window,
Go in and out the window,
Go in and out the window
As you have done before.

Now come and face your partner,
Now come and face your partner,
Now come and face your partner
As you have done before.

Now follow me to London,
Now follow me to London,
Now follow me to London
As you have done before.

Go in and out the window,
Go in and out the window,
Go in and out the window
As you have done before.

16 Bluebird, Bluebird

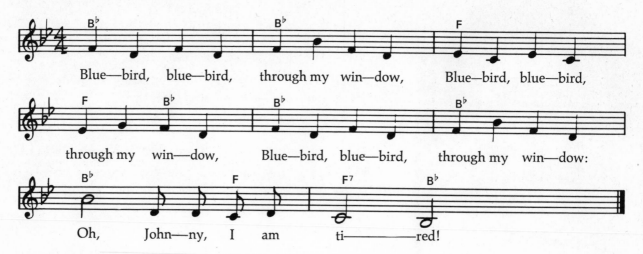

Blue—bird, blue—bird, through my win—dow, Blue—bird, blue—bird,

through my win—dow, Blue—bird, blue—bird, through my win—dow:

Oh, John—ny, I am ti————red!

Bluebird, bluebird, through my window,
Bluebird, bluebird, through my window,
Bluebird, bluebird, through my window:
    Oh, Johnny, I am tired!

Take a little girl and tap her on the shoulder,
Take a little girl and tap her on the shoulder,
Take a little girl and tap her on the shoulder:
    Oh, Johnny, I am tired!

Bluebird, bluebird, through my window,
Bluebird, bluebird, through my window,
Bluebird, bluebird, through my window:
    Oh, Johnny, I am tired!

17 King William was King George's son

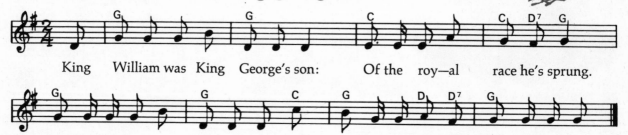

King William was King George's son: Of the roy—al race he's sprung.

He had a star u——pon his breast With points to the east and points to the west.

King William was King George's son:
Of the royal race he's sprung.
He had a star upon his breast
With points to the east and points to the west.

Upon the carpet you shall kneel
While the grass grows in the field.
Stand up straight upon your feet
And choose the one you love so sweet.

 Now they're married, wish them joy:
First a girl and then a boy.
Seven years after, seven years to come:
Fire on the mountain, kiss and run.

Green gra—vel, green gra—vel, The grass grows so green, The fairest young maiden That e—ver was seen. Green gravel, green gravel, Your true love is dead, So I sent you a message To turn out your head.

19 Rise, Sally, rise

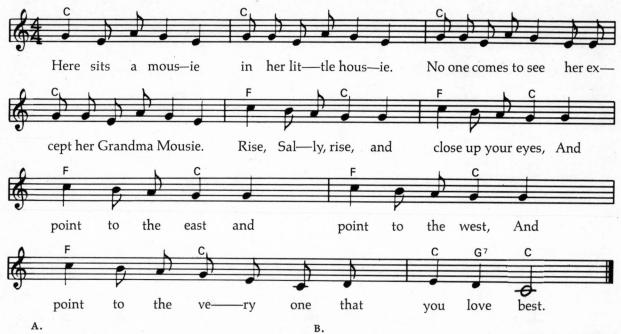

Here sits a mous—ie in her lit—tle hous—ie. No one comes to see her ex—cept her Grandma Mousie. Rise, Sal—ly, rise, and close up your eyes, And point to the east and point to the west, And point to the ve—ry one that you love best.

A.

Little Sally Waters, sitting in the sun,
Crying and weeping for a young man.
Rise, Sally, rise, and dry out your eyes.
Point to the east and point to the west
And point to the one that you love best.

B.

Here sits a mousie in her little housie.
No one comes to see her except her Grandma Mousie.
Rise, Sally, rise, and close up your eyes,
And point to the east and point to the west,
And point to the very one that you love best.

20 Going to Chicago

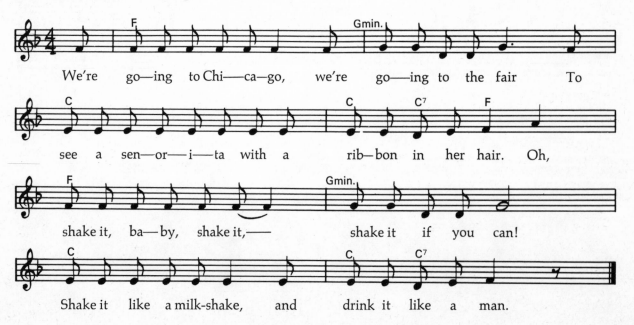

We're go—ing to Chi—ca—go, we're go—ing to the fair To see a sen—or—i—ta with a rib—bon in her hair. Oh, shake it, ba—by, shake it,—— shake it if you can! Shake it like a milk-shake, and drink it like a man.

21 Old Roger is dead

Old Roger is dead and he lies in his grave,
Lies in his grave, lies in his grave.
Old Roger is dead and he lies in his grave,
Hi, ho, lies in his grave.

Old Roger is dead and he lies in his grave,
Lies in his grave, lies in his grave.
Old Roger is dead and he lies in his grave,
Hi, ho, lies in his grave.

They planted an apple tree over his head,
Over his head, over his head.
They planted an apple tree over his head,
Hi, ho, over his head.

The apples got ripe and they fell to the ground,
Fell to the ground, fell to the ground.
The apples got ripe and they fell to the ground,
Hi, ho, fell to the ground.

There came an old lady a-picking them up,
Picking them up, picking them up.
There came an old lady a-picking them up,
Hi, ho, picking them up.

Old Roger got up and he gave her a thump,
Gave her a thump, gave her a thump.
Old Roger got up and he gave her a thump,
Hi, ho, gave her a thump.

22 The jolly old miller

There's a jol—ly old mil—ler and he lives by himself. As the
wheel goes a—round he's a mer—ry old elf. One hand in the hop—per and the
o—ther in the bag, As the wheel comes a—round he cries out: "GRAB!"

23 The pig in the parlour

TUNE: FOR HE'S A JOLLY GOOD FELLOW

We have a pig in the parlour,
We have a pig in the parlour,
We have a pig in the parlour
And he's a Scotsman too.
  And he's a Scotsman too,
  And he's a Scotsman too.
  We have a pig in the parlour
  And he's a Scotsman too.

Your right hand to your partner,
Your left hand to your neighbour.
Your right hand to your partner
For he's a Scotman too.
  For he's a Scotsman too,
  For he's a Scotsman too.
  Your right hand to your neighbour
  For he's a Scotsman too.

We have a new pig in the parlour . . .
or: We've the same old pig in the parlour . . .

BRIDGE GAMES

24 *London Bridge*

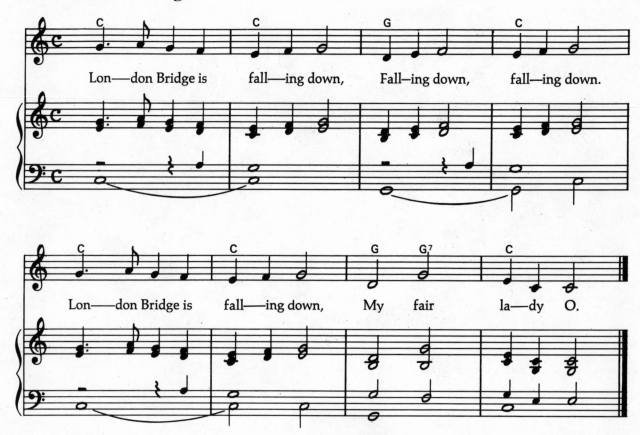

Lon——don Bridge is fall——ing down, Fall—ing down, fall—ing down.

Lon——don Bridge is fall——ing down, My fair la—dy O.

London Bridge is falling down,
Falling down, falling down.
London Bridge is falling down,
  My fair lady O.

London Bridge is half built up,
Half built up, half built up.
London Bridge is half built up,
  My fair lady O.

London Bridge is all built up,
All built up, all built up.
London Bridge is all built up,
  My fair lady O.

Chop their heads off one by one,
One by one, one by one.
Chop their heads off one by one,
  My fair lady O.

Get the keys and lock her up,
Lock her up, lock her up.
Get the keys and lock her up,
  My fair lady O.

25 *The robbers coming through*

TUNE: LONDON BRIDGE (NO. 24)

Here are the robbers coming through,
Coming through, coming through.
Here are the robbers coming through,
    My fair lady O.

What did the robbers do to you,
Do to you, do to you?
What did the robbers do to you,
    My fair lady O?

Broke my watch and stole my chain,
Stole my chain, stole my chain.
Broke my watch and stole my chain,
    My fair lady O.

Off to prison he must go,
He must go, he must go.
Off to prison he must go,
    My fair lady O.

26 *Oranges and lemons*

Oran—ges and le—mons, Say the bells of St. Clem—ents. You owe me five farthings, Say the bells of St. Mar—tin's.

Oranges and lemons,
Say the bells of St. Clements.

You owe me five farthings,
Say the bells of St. Martin's.

When will you pay me?
Say the bells of Old Bailey.

When I grow rich,
Say the bells of Shoreditch.

When will that be?
Say the bells of Stepney.

I'm sure I don't know,
Says the great bell of Bow.

Here comes a candle to light you to bed,
And here comes a chopper to chop off your head!

LINE
GAMES

27 Nuts in May

TUNE: THE MULBERRY BUSH (NO. 8)

Here we go gathering nuts in May,
Nuts in May, nuts in May.
Here we go gathering nuts in May
On a cold and frosty morning.

Who will you have for nuts in May,
Nuts in May, nuts in May?
Who will you have for nuts in May
On a cold and frosty morning?

We'll have Mary Jones for nuts in May,
Nuts in May, nuts in May.
We'll have Mary Jones for nuts in May
On a cold and frosty morning.

Who will you have to pull her away,
Pull her away, pull her away?
Who will you have to pull her away
On a cold and frosty morning?

We'll have Fanny Brown to pull her away,
Pull her away, pull her away.
We'll have Fanny Brown to pull her away
On a cold and frosty morning.

. . . .

28 Jinny Jo

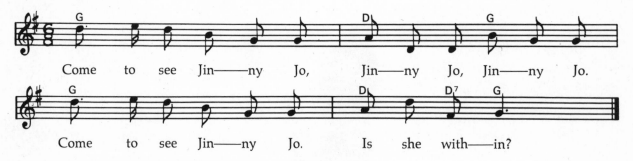

Come to see Jinny Jo, Jinny Jo, Jinny Jo.
Come to see Jinny Jo. Is she within?

Jinny Jo's washing clothes, washing clothes, washing clothes.
Jinny Jo's washing clothes. Can't see her today.

REFRAIN: Fare you well, ladies, O ladies, O ladies!
Fare you well, ladies, and gentlemen, too!

32

Come to see Jinny Jo, Jinny Jo, Jinny Jo.
Come to see Jinny Jo. Is she within?

    Jinny Jo's ironing clothes, ironing clothes, ironing clothes.
    Jinny Jo's ironing clothes. Can't see her today.

REFRAIN

Come to see Jinny Jo, Jinny Jo, Jinny Jo.
Come to see Jinny Jo. Is she within?

    Jinny Jo's dead and gone, dead and gone, dead and gone.
    Jinny Jo's dead and gone. Can't see her today.

REFRAIN

What shall we dress her in, dress her in, dress her in?
What shall we dress her in? Shall it be red?

    Red is for the soldiers, the soldiers, the soldiers.
    Red is for the soldiers, so that will not do.

REFRAIN

What shall we dress her in, dress her in, dress her in?
What shall we dress her in? Shall it be blue?

    Blue is for the sailors, the sailors, the sailors.
    Blue is for the sailors, so that will not do.

REFRAIN

What shall we dress her in, dress her in, dress her in?
What shall we dress her in? Shall it be black?

    Black is for the mourners, the mourners, the mourners.
    Black is for the mourners, so that will just do.

REFRAIN

29 We've come from Spain

We've come from Spain, we've come from Spain
To call upon your daughter Jane.

My daughter Jane is far too young
To be called on by anyone.

Oh, very well, we'll go away
And come again some other day.

Come back, come back, our house is free,
And choose the fairest one you see.

The fairest one that I can see
Is Molly Brown – come out to me.

30 The English soldiers

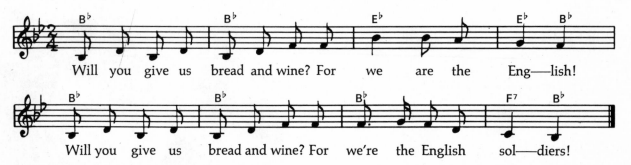

Will you give us bread and wine?
For we are the English!
Will you give us bread and wine?
For we're the English soldiers!

We won't give you bread and wine,
For we are the French!
We won't give you bread and wine,
For we're the French soldiers!

Are you ready for a fight?
For we are the English!
Are you ready for a fight?
For we're the English soldiers!

Yes, we're ready for a fight,
For we are the French!
Yes, we're ready for a fight,
For we're the French soldiers!

Now we're on the battlefield,
For we are the English!
Now we're on the battlefield,
For we're the English soldiers!

SHOOT!

BANG!

FIRE!

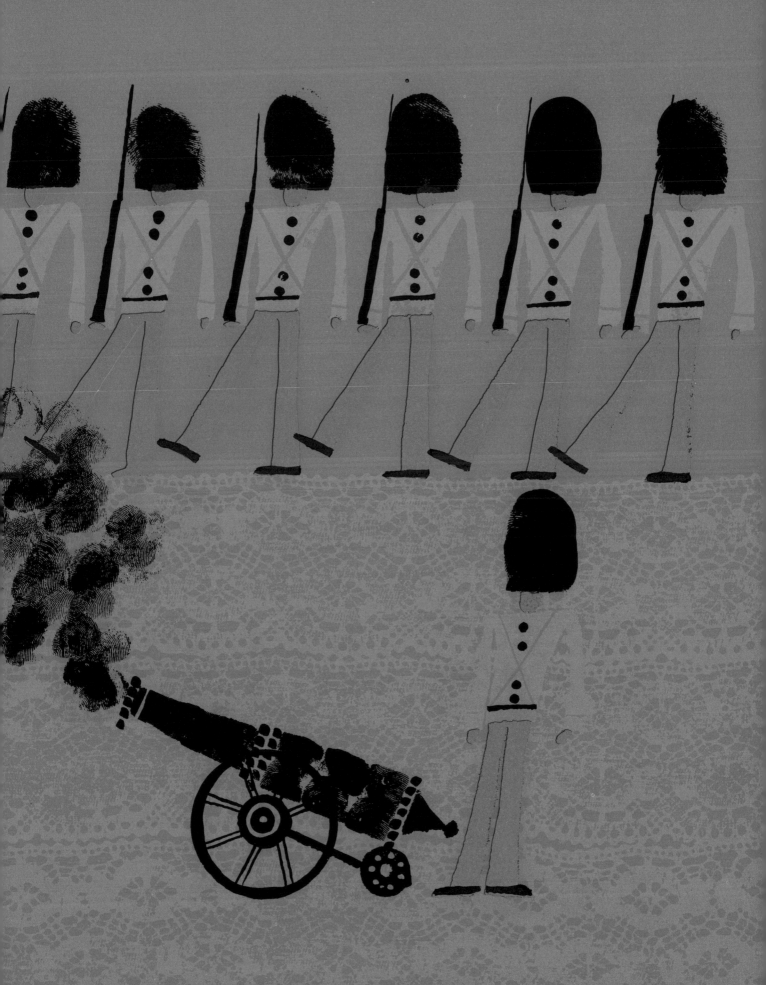

31 Three kings a-riding

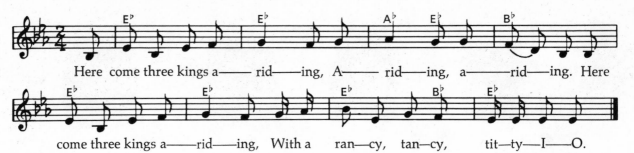

Here come three kings a——rid——ing, A——rid—ing, a——rid—ing. Here
come three kings a——rid—ing, With a ran—cy, tan—cy, tit—ty—I—O.

Here come three kings a-riding,
A-riding, a-riding.
Here come three kings a-riding,
With a rancy, tancy, titty-I-O.

We're coming here to get married,
Married, married.
We're coming here to get married,
With a rancy, tancy, titty-I-O.

What are you coming here for,
Here for, here for?
What are you coming here for,
With a rancy, tancy, titty-I-O?

Which one will you have, sirs,
Have, sirs, have, sirs?
Which one will you have, sirs,
With a rancy, tancy, titty-I-O?

I think I will take this one,
This one, this one.
I think I will take this one,
With a rancy, tancy, titty-I-O.

 ASSORTED GAMES

32 A-hunting we will go

A——hunting we will go! A——hunting we will go! We'll
catch a little fox and put him in a box, And ne—ver let him go.

33 The grand old Duke of York

The grand old Duke of York, He had ten thou—sand men. He marched them up to the top of the hill And marched them down a——gain.

The grand old Duke of York,
He had ten thousand men.
He marched them up to the top of the hill
And marched them down again.

And when they were up, they were up,
And when they were down, they were down,
And when they were only half way up
They were neither up nor down.

34 The white ship sails

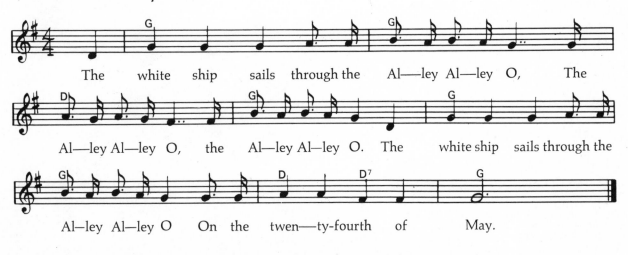

The white ship sails through the Al—ley Al—ley O, The Al—ley Al—ley O, the Al—ley Al—ley O. The white ship sails through the Al—ley Al—ley O On the twen—ty-fourth of May.

35 Jim-a-long Josie

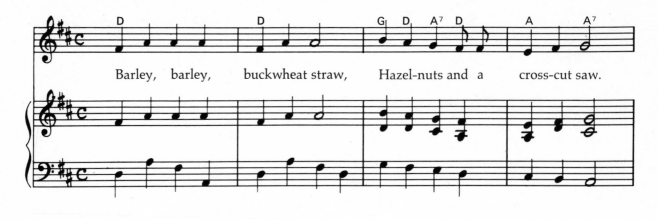

Barley, barley, buckwheat straw, Hazel-nuts and a cross-cut saw.

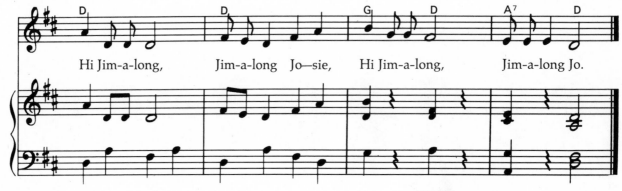

Hi Jim-a-long, Jim-a-long Jo—sie, Hi Jim-a-long, Jim-a-long Jo.

Barley, barley, buckwheat straw,
Hazel-nuts and a cross-cut saw.
Hi Jim-a-long, Jim-a-long Josie,
Hi Jim-a-long, Jim-a-long Jo.

Any pretty girl that wants a beau
Fall in the arms of Jim-a-long Jo.
Hi Jim-a-long, Jim-a-long Josie,
Hi Jim-a-long, Jim-a-long Jo.

I went to the river and I couldn't get across.
I paid five cents for an old grey horse.
Hi Jim-a-long, Jim-a-long Josie,
Hi Jim-a-long, Jim-a-long Jo.

Say, my love, will you go to Boston?
Say, my love, will you go to Boston?
Say, my love, will you go to Boston
    Early in the morning?

Yes, my love, I'll go to Boston,
Yes, my love, I'll go to Boston,
Yes, my love, I'll go to Boston
    Early in the morning.

What will we do when we get to Boston?
What will we do when we get to Boston?
What will we do when we get to Boston
    Early in the morning?

We'll get married when we get to Boston,
We'll get married when we get to Boston,
We'll get married when we get to Boston
    Early in the morning.

37 *Miss Polly had a dolly*

Miss Pol—ly had a dol—ly who was sick, sick, sick, So she

called for the doc—tor to come quick, quick, quick. The

Miss Polly had a dolly who was sick, sick, sick,
So she called for the doctor to come quick, quick, quick.
The doctor came with his bag and his hat
And he rapped on the door with a rat tat tat.

38 *I'm a little Dutch girl*

TUNE: DID YOU EVER SEE A LASSIE? (NO. 13)

I'm a little Dutch girl,
A Dutch girl, a Dutch girl.
I'm a little Dutch girl,
A Dutch girl am I.
  I'm a little Dutch boy,
  A Dutch boy, a Dutch boy.
  I'm a little Dutch boy,
  A Dutch boy am I.

Oh, go away, I hate you,
I hate you, I hate you.
Oh, go away, I hate you,
I hate you, I do!
  Oh, why do you hate me,
  Oh, hate me, oh, hate me?
  Oh, why do you hate me,
  Oh, hate me you do?

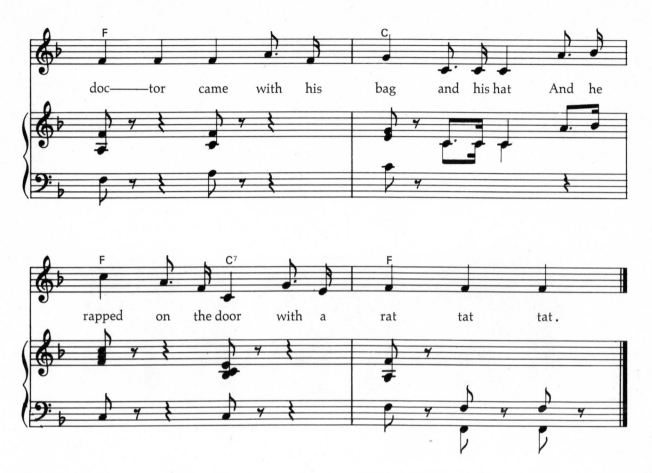

doc——tor came with his bag and his hat And he
rapped on the door with a rat tat tat.

He looked at the dolly and shook his head,
And he said, "Miss Polly, put her straight to bed."
He wrote on some paper for a pill, pill, pill.
"I'll be back in the morning with the bill, bill, bill."

Because you stole my necklace,
My necklace, my necklace.
Because you stole my necklace,
My necklace you stole.
  Oh, here is your necklace,
  Your necklace, your necklace.
  Oh, here is your necklace,
  Your necklace I stole.

Oh, now we're getting married,
Getting married, getting married.
Oh, now we're getting married,
Getting married are we!

39 No bears out tonight

No bears out to——night, No bears out to—night,

No bears out to-night – They've all gone a———way!

40 One little elephant balancing

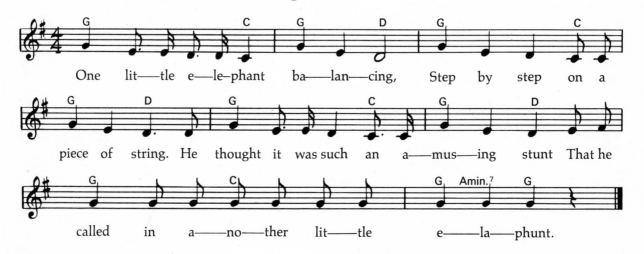

One lit——tle e—le–phant ba——lan——cing, Step by step on a

piece of string. He thought it was such an a——mus——ing stunt That he

called in a—no—ther lit——tle e——la—phunt.

One little elephant balancing,
Step by step on a piece of string.
He thought it was such an amusing stunt
That he called in another little elaphunt.

Two little elephants balancing,
Step by step on a piece of string.
They thought it was such an amusing stunt
That they called in another little elaphunt.

Three little elephants balancing . . .

41 *If you're happy*

If you're hap—py and you know it, clap your hands *(clap, clap)*. If you're hap—py and you know it, clap your hands *(clap, clap)*. If you're hap—py and you know it, then you real—ly ought to show it. If you're hap——py and you know it, clap your hands *(clap, clap)*.

* occasionally, for variety

44

If you're happy and you know it, clap your hands (*clap, clap*).
If you're happy and you know it, clap your hands (*clap, clap*).
If you're happy and you know it, then you really ought to show it.
If you're happy and you know it, clap your hands (*clap, clap*).

If you're happy and you know it, stamp your feet (*stamp, stamp*).
If you're happy and you know it, stamp your feet (*stamp, stamp*).
If you're happy and you know it, then you really ought to show it.
If you're happy and you know it, stamp your feet (*stamp, stamp*).

{ Repeat for: "snap your fingers,"
"slap your sides,"
"shout 'Hurray!'" and
"do all five."

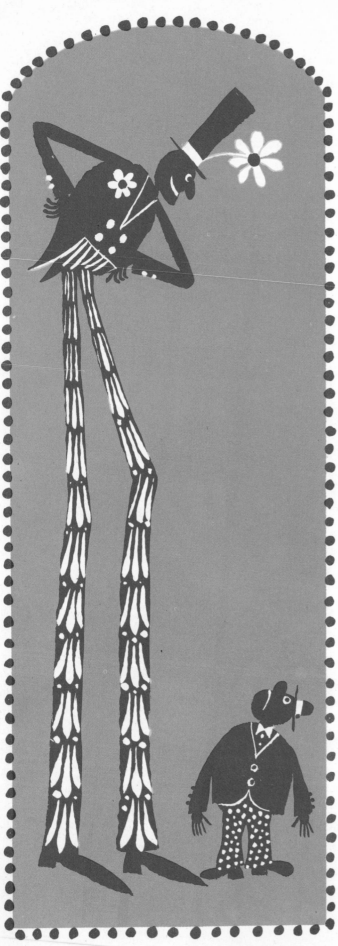

42 Old Daddy Tom

Who goes round my house this dark night?
– Old Daddy Tom with his nightcap on.
What does he want? – A good fat sheep.
  Take the worst and leave the best,
  And don't come back to bother the rest.

43 Head and shoulders

TUNE: LONDON BRIDGE (NO. 24)

Head and shoulders, knees and toes,
Knees and toes, knees and toes!
Head and shoulders, knees and toes,
Clap your hands and around you go!

44 It doesn't really matter

TUNE: JOHN BROWN'S BODY

It doesn't really matter if you weren't born tall.
It doesn't really matter if you weren't born tall.
It doesn't really matter if you weren't born tall.
Stand tall! Stand tall! Stand tall!

SKIPPING
RHYMES

45

A.

Not last night but the night before
Twenty-four robbers came to my door.
This is what they said to me:
    Lady, turn around, turn around, turn around.
    Lady, touch the ground, touch the ground, touch the ground.
    Lady, show your shoe, show your shoe, show your shoe.
    Lady, that will do, that will do, that will do!

B.

Not last night but the night before
Three little robbers came knockin' at my door.
One had a fiddle, one had a drum,
One had a stick-stack stuck to his bum.

46

Girl Guide, Girl Guide, dressed in blue,
These are the motions you must do:
    Stand at attention; stand at ease.
    Bend your elbows; bend your knees.
    Salute to the captain; bow to the queen;
    Turn your back on the dirty submarine.
    I can do the heel-toe; I can do the splits.
    I can do the wiggle-waggle just like this!

Girl Guide, Girl Guide, dressed in green,
The leader sent me to the queen.
The queen didn't want me, sent me to the king.
The king said: "Turn around and count to seventeen."
1, 2, 3, 4, 5, 6, 7, 8, 9, 10, 11, 12, 13, 14, 15, 16, 17.

Girl Guide, Girl Guide, dressed in yellow,
This is the way I treat my fellow:
Hug him, kiss him, kick him in the pants –
That is the way to find romance.

Girl Guide, Girl Guide, dressed in red,
What time do you go to bed?
One o'clock, two o'clock, three o'clock . . .

47

A.

Cinderella dressed in yella
Went upstairs to kiss her fella.
How many kisses did she get?
1, 2, 3, 4, 5 . . .

B.

Cinderella dressed in lace
Went upstairs to powder her face.
How many pounds did it take?
2, 4, 6, 8, 2, 4, 6, 8 . . .

Cinderella dressed in red
Went downstairs to bake some bread.
How many loaves did she make?
1, 2, 3, 4, 5, . . .

C.

Mary, Mary, all dressed in yellow
Went upstairs to kiss her fellow.
Made a mistake and kissed a snake
And came downstairs with a belly-ache.

48

Spanish dancer, do the split, split, split.
Spanish dancer, do the kick, kick, kick.
Spanish dancer, turn around, round, round.
Spanish dancer, touch the ground, ground, ground.
Spanish dancer, get out of town, town, town.

49

Teddy bear, teddy bear, turn around.
Teddy bear, teddy bear, touch the ground.
Teddy bear, teddy bear, show your shoe.
Teddy bear, teddy bear, that will do.

Teddy bear, teddy bear, go upstairs.
Teddy bear, teddy bear, say your prayers.
Teddy bear, teddy bear, switch off the light.
Teddy bear, teddy bear, say goodnight.
GOODNIGHT!

50

A.

I had a little teddy bear, his name was Tiny Tim.
I put him in the bathtub to see if he could swim.
He drank all the water; he ate all the soap;
He died the next morning with a bubble in his throat.

In came the doctor; in came the nurse;
In came a lady with a big fat purse.
Out went the doctor, out went the nurse,
Out went the lady with the big fat purse.

B.

Miss Lucy had a baby; she called him Tiny Tim.
She put him in a bathtub to see if he could swim.
He drank up all the water and ate up all the soap;
He died the next morning with bubbles in his throat.

Miss Lucy called the doctor; Miss Lucy called the nurse;
Miss Lucy called the lady with the alligator purse.
In walked the doctor; in walked the nurse;
In walked the lady with the alligator purse.

"Penicillin," said the doctor. "Penicillin," said the nurse.
"Penicillin," said the lady with the alligator purse.
 Out walked the doctor; out walked the nurse;
 Out walked the lady with Tim in her purse.

51

A.

Mother, mother, I feel ill:
Send for the doctor on the hill.
Doctor, doctor, will I live?
Yes, no, maybe so. Yes, no, maybe so . . .

B.

Mother, mother, I am sick.
Send for the doctor quick, quick, quick.
Doctor, doctor, will I die?
Yes, my darling, by and by.

52

Johnny's got the whooping cough
And Mary's got the measles.
That's the way the money goes:
Pop goes the weasel!

A penny for a spool of thread,
A penny for a needle.
That's the way the money goes:
Pop goes the weasel!

53

Old Man Moses, sick in bed,
He called for the doctor, and this is what he said:
"Take two steps forward and turn yourself around.
Do the wiggle-waggle and get out of town."

54

Policeman, policeman, do your duty.
Here comes Janie, the bathing beauty.
She can do the heel-toe; she can do the splits;
She can do the wiggle-waggle just like this!

55 There came a girl from France

There came a girl from France: She didn't know how to dance. The on—ly thing that she could do Was "Knees up, Mother Brown!" Oh, knees up, Mother Brown! Knees up, Mother Brown! Knees up, knees up, never let the breeze up! Knees up, Mother Brown.

There came a girl from France:
She didn't know how to dance.
The only thing that she could do
Was "Knees up, Mother Brown!"

REFRAIN:
Oh, knees up, Mother Brown!
Knees up, Mother Brown!
Knees up, knees up, never let the breeze up!
Knees up, Mother Brown.

Oh, hopping on one foot,
Hopping on one foot,
Hopping, hopping, never stopping,
Hopping on one foot.

Oh, hopping on the other,
Hopping on the other.
Hopping, hopping, never stopping,
Hopping on the other.

Oh, twirling round and round,
Twirling round and round,
Twirling, twirling, never whirling,
Twirling round and round.

56

I went down town to see Miss Brown.
She gave me a nickel to buy a pickle.
The pickle was sour: she gave me a flower.
The flower was dead: she gave me a thread.
The thread was black: she gave me a smack.
The smack was hard: she gave me a card,
And this is what the card said to do:
    Lady, turn around, turn around, turn around.
    Lady, touch the ground, touch the ground, touch the ground.
    Lady, show your shoe, show your shoe, show your shoe.
    Lady, that will do, that will do, that will do.

57
Three chairs,
Sit me down.
Cross my legs
And turn around.

58
Mickey Mouse
Ran through the house.
Clapped his hands,
Stamped his feet,
Wiggled his tail,
And around about!

59
Bow, wow, wow!
Whose dog art thou?
Little Tommy Tinker's dog,
Bow, wow, wow!

60

Donald Duck is a one-legged, one-legged, one-legged duck.
Donald Duck is a two-legged, two-legged, two-legged duck.
Donald Duck is a three-legged, three-legged, three-legged duck.
Donald Duck is a four-legged, four-legged, four-legged duck.
Donald Duck is a bow-legged, bow-legged, bow-legged duck.
Donald Duck is a pigeon-toed, pigeon-toed, pigeon-toed duck.

61
Ice cream soda, lemonade tart,
Tell me the name of your sweetheart.
A, B, C, D, E . . .

62
Bread and butter, sugar and spice,
How many boys think I'm nice?
1, 2, 3, 4, 5 . . .

63

A.

All in together, girls!
First by the weather, girls!
When you call your birthday
You must fall out.
January, February, March . . .

When you call your date
You must fall out.
1, 2, 3, 4, 5 . . .

When you call your first initial
You must fall out.
A, B, C, D, E . . .

When you call your second initial
You must fall out.
A, B, C, D, E . . .

When you call your third initial
You must fall out.
A, B, C, D, E . . .

B.

All in together girls!
This fine weather, girls!
I saw the preacher kiss the teacher.
How many kisses did she give him?
1, 2, 3, 4, 5 . . .

C.

All in together, girls!
This fine weather, girls!
I spy a nanny goat
Hanging by its petticoat.
If I call your name
You must run out . . .

D.

All in together, girls!
This stormy weather, girls!
Put your hats and jackets on –
Tell your mother you won't be long:
Just around the corner.
Red hot pepper!

64

Grapes on the vine
Ready to be picked.
One·fell off
And the other did the splits.

65

Apples, peaches, pears, and plums,
Tell me when your birthday comes.
January, February, March . . .

66

Bluebells, cockle-shells,
Eevy, ivy, over.
My mother sent me to the store,
And this is what she sent me for:
Salt, vinegar, mustard, pepper,
Salt, vinegar, mustard, pepper . . .

67

Mabel, Mabel,
Set the table.
Don't forget the
Salt, mustard, vinegar, pepper,
Salt, mustard, vinegar, pepper . . .

68

Peel a banana upside down.
Peel an orange round and round.
If you jump to twenty-four,
You can have your turn once more.
1, 2, 3, 4, 5 . . .

69

Jelly in the bowl,
Jelly in the bowl,
Wibble wabble, wibble wabble,
Jelly in the bowl.

70

Two little sausages
Frying in a pan.
One went pop
And the other went BAM!

71

I had a little chicken
And he wouldn't lay an egg,
So I poured hot chocolate
Up and down his leg,
And he wiggled and he jiggled,
And he stood on his head.
Funny little chickie
Laid a hard-boiled **egg**.

72

Polly, put the kettle on
And have a cup of tea.
In comes Janie,
And out goes me.

73

Andy Pandy,
Sugar and candy,
I pop in.

Andy Pandy,
Sugar and candy,
I pop up.

Andy Pandy,
Sugar and candy,
I pop down.

Andy Pandy,
Sugar and candy,
I pop out.

74

My father was a butcher,
My mother cuts the meat,
And I'm the little hot dog
That runs around the street.

75

My father is a garbage man –
Pheew!
My mother is a baker –
Pheew! Yum yum!

My sister is a hairdresser –
Pheew! Yum yum! Curl curl!
My brother is a cowboy –
Pheew! Yum yum! Curl curl! Bang bang!
My baby is a cry-baby –
Pheew! Yum yum! Curl curl! Bang bang! Waaaa!

76

My mother and Nancy's mother
Live across the street.
Every time they have a fight

This is what they say:
    Ickabacker, ickabacker, ickabacker boo!
    Ickabacker, soda cracker, out goes you!

77

My mother and your mother
Were hanging out the clothes.
My mother gave your mother
A punch on the nose.
What colour was the blood? – Blue!
B-L-U-E spells blue, and out you must go
As fast as your little slippers will carry you.

78

TUNE: TRAMP, TRAMP, TRAMP, THE BOYS ARE MARCHING

Vote, vote, vote for dear old Janie!
Who's that knocking at the door?
If it's Linda, let her in,
And we'll sock her on the chin,
And we won't vote for Janie any more.
Two, four, shut the door. Run out!

79

TUNE: THE FARMER IN THE DELL (NO. 5)

Somebody's under the bed.
Whoever can it be?
I'm getting kinda nervous,
So Janie, come in with me.

Janie lit the candle,
And under the bed she went.
Get up, Jane! Get up, Jane!
There's somebody under the bed!

80

Here comes teacher with a red hot stick.
Wonder what I got in arithmetic?
10, 20, 30, 40, 50 . . .

Here comes the teacher yelling.
Wonder what I got in spelling?
10, 20, 30, 40, 50 . . .

81

Teacher, teacher, with the red hot stick:
Are you ready for arithmetic?
One and one? – Two. Two and two? – Four.

Are you ready for your spelling?
Cat? – C-A-T. Dog? – D-O-G.

Are you ready for your exercise?
Up, down, around, and out.

82

Mr. Green is a very nice man,
Tries to teach you all he can:
Reading, writing, arithmetic –
But he never fails to give the stick.
If he does, you will jump
Out of England, into France,
Out of France, into Spain,
Out of Spain, back home again.

83

Sitting in the school-room
Chewing bubble gum.
In comes the principal –
And out goes the gum!

84

Dancing Dolly had no sense.
She bought a fiddle for fifteen cents.
The only tune that she could play
Was "Over the Hills and Far Away."

Over the hills and far away there was a school,
And in that school there was a room,
And in that room there was a stool,
And on that stool there was a fool,
And the fool is Polly Perkins.

85

Two in a hammock just about to kiss,
When all of a sudden the darn thing slipped.

86

Two little cars, two little kisses:
Two weeks later, Mister and Missus.

87

Cowboy Joe
Went to Mexico.
Hands up! Stick 'em up!
Cowboy Joe.

Cowboy Joe
Broke his toe
Riding on a buffalo.

Cowboy Joe
Broke his back
Riding on a railway track.

88

Nine o'clock is striking.
Mother, may I go out?
All the boys are waiting
Just to get me out.

First she gave me an apple,
Second she gave me a pear,
Then she gave me a clout
That sent me under the stair.

89

A.

House to let, apply within.
Jenny jump out and Jean jump in.

B.

House to let, apply within.
The lady upstairs is drinking gin.
Now drinking gin is a very bad thing,
So when I go out, let Mary come in.

90

As I was in the kitchen
Doing a little stitchin',
In popped a bogey-man,
Out popped me.

91

Miss Monroe broke her toe
Riding on a buffalo.
The buffalo died and Miss Monroe cried,
And that was the end of the buffalo ride.

Miss Monroe broke her head
Riding on a slice of bread.
The slice of bread broke and Miss Monroe choked,
And that is the end of this funny, funny joke.

92

The King and the Queen
And the partners, too.
The next King and Queen
Will pass right through.

93

Old Mother Witch
Fell in the ditch,
Picked up a penny,
And thought she was rich.

94

Die, die, little dog, die.
Die for the sake of your grandmother's eye.
A penny to put in your purse,
A penny to pay the nurse.
Die, die, little dog, die.
Die for the sake of your grandmother's eye.

95

Yankee Doodle went to town
Riding on a pony.
He stuck a feather in his hat
And called it macaroni.

Yankee Doodle went to town
Riding on a pony.
He stuck his head in a beauty shop
And came out with a Toni.

96

Charlie Chaplin went to France
To teach the ladies how to dance.
Heel, toe, round you go.
How many ladies did he teach?
1, 2, 3, 4, 5 . . .

97

Funny Bob Hope,
Silly as a dope.
Wiggle waggle, wiggle waggle,
Funny Bob Hope.

98

Jill had an ear-ache,
She didn't know what to do.
She put her finger in her ear
And cracked it right in two.

99

Fudge, fudge, tell the judge
Janie's having a baby.
Oh, joy, it's a boy!
Janie's going crazy.
Wrap it up in tissue paper,
Send it down the elevator.
How many pounds does it weigh?
1, 2, 3, 4, 5 . . .

100

Alouette-a, smoke a cigarette-a,
Chew tobacco, spit it on the floor.
In comes Nancy, spank her little bumbo.
Ouch! Ouch! Ouch! Don't you do it any more.

101

Down in Czechoslovaky
Where the men chew tobaccy
And the women go wiggle-waggle-woo.

102

A.
I had a little Dutch car
In nineteen forty-eight.
I took it down to Main Street
And put on the brake.

B.
I had a little car
And it went "Peep! Peep!"
I took it round the cor-ner
And across the street.

C.
Had a little Austin in nineteen forty-eight.
Turned around the corner and slammed on the brake.
Policeman caught me, put me in jail.
All I had was ginger-ale.
How many gallons did I drink?
2, 4, 6, 8 . . .

103

Maggie and Jiggs went down town.
Maggie bought a rolling pin to knock Jiggs down.
How many times did she hit him?
1, 2, 3, 4, 5 . . .

104

Blondie and Dagwood went up town.
Blondie bought an evening gown.
Dagwood bought the *Daily News*,
And this is what it said:
    Close your eyes and count to ten.
    If you miss, you take the end.
    1, 2, 3, 4, 5, 6, 7, 8, 9, 10.

105

Salami was a dancer:
She danced for the king,
    And every time she danced
    She wiggled everything.
"Stop!" said the king,
"You can't do that in here."
"Pooh!" said Salami
    And kicked him in the rear.

106

I'm Popeye the sailor man.
I live in a garbage can.
I love to go swimmin'
With bare naked wimmin.
I'm Popeye the sailor man.

107

Tillie the Toiler
Never late.
She's always at the office
At half-past eight.

108

TUNE: LITTLE BROWN JUG

I love coffee, I love tea,
I love the boys, and the boys love me.
Tell my mother to hold her tongue,
She had a boy when she was young.
Tell my father to do the same:
He had a girl and he changed her name.

109

Lord Nelson lost his eye.
Lord Nelson lost his arm.
Lord Nelson lost his leg
In the Battle of Newfoundland.

Lord Nelson found his eye.
Lord Nelson found his arm.
Lord Nelson found his leg
In the Battle of Newfoundland.

110

Christopher Columbus sailed the sea,
Huckleberry treasures all for me,
And the waves went higher, higher, higher.

111

Christopher Columbus sailed the ocean blue
In fourteen hundred and ninety-two.
He sailed so far on the deep blue sea
That he didn't get back till fourteen ninety-three.

112

Old Man Daisy
He went crazy.
Up the ladder, down the ladder,
Over my head.

113

Hi, Ricky Nelson, how about a date?
I'll meet you at the corner at half-past eight.
Yes, no, yes, no . . .

114 *The wind, the wind*

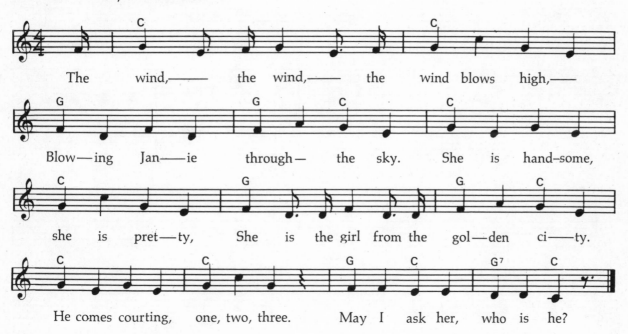

The wind, the wind, the wind blows high,

Blow—ing Jan—ie through — the sky. She is hand–some,

she is pret—ty, She is the girl from the gol—den ci—ty.

He comes courting, one, two, three. May I ask her, who is he?

A.

The wind, the wind, the wind blows high,
Blowing Janie through the sky.
She is handsome, she is pretty,
She is the girl from the golden city.
He comes courting, one, two, three.
May I ask her, who is he?

Michael Gray says he loves her.
All the girls come crowding round her.
Open the box, show her the ring –
Tomorrow, tomorrow, the wedding begins.
Open the box, show her the ring –
Tomorrow, tomorrow, the wedding begins!

B.

The wind, the wind, the wind blows high,
Blowing Heather through the sky.
She is sick and going to die.
Oh, Michael, I love you!

Michael, Michael, says he loves her.
Michael, Michael, says he loves her.
Michael, Michael, says he loves her.
Oh, Michael, I love you!

On a mountain

On a mountain stands a la—dy. Who she is I do not know.

All she wants is gold and sil—ver; All she needs is a nice young man. So

call in my No—ra dear, No—ra dear, No—ra dear, So

call in my No—ra dear while I go out to play (hit the hay!).

116 Doctor, doctor

Doc—tor, doc—tor, can you tell What will make poor Shei—la well?

She is sick and going to die – That will make poor Tom—my cry.

Doctor, doctor, can you tell
What will make poor Sheila well?
She is sick and going to die –
That will make poor Tommy cry.

Tommy, Tommy, don't you cry.
You will see her by and by,
Dressed in pink or navy blue,
Waiting at the church to marry you.

117 Down in the valley

Down in the valley where the green grass grows,
There stands Janie, pretty as a rose.
She sang and she sang and she sang so sweet,
Along came a little boy and kissed her on the cheek.

Oh, Janie, you ought to be ashamed!
You kissed a little boy and don't know his name!
He took her to the big house, set her on his knee,
Asked her a question, "Will you marry me?"
Yes, no, maybe so, yes, no, maybe so . . .

118 Rosy apple, lemon, and pear

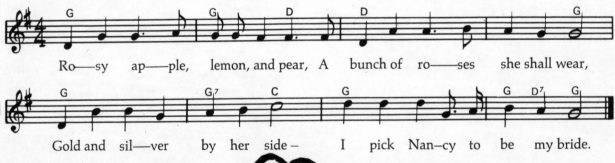

Ro—sy ap—ple, lemon, and pear, A bunch of ro—ses she shall wear,

Gold and sil—ver by her side – I pick Nan—cy to be my bride.

Rosy apple, lemon, and pear,
A bunch of roses she shall wear,
Gold and silver by her side –
I pick Nancy to be my bride.

Take her by the lily-white hand,
Take her to the altar stand.
Give her kisses, one, two, three.
Old Mother Hubbard stuck a pin in me!

119 All the boys in our town

All the boys in our town   lead a   hap–py life,   All   except   Jim——my, and

he   shall have   a   wife.   A   wife   he   shall have,   and   a-

courting he   will go   A——long   with   Ja—nie   be–cause he loves her so.

All the boys in our town lead a happy life,
All except Jimmy, and he shall have a wife.
A wife he shall have, and a-courting he will go
Along with Janie because he loves her so.

He loves her, he loves her, he sits her on his knee
And says, "Dearest Janie, will you marry me?"
She flushes, she blushes, she doesn't know what to say.
Next Sunday morning will be the wedding day.

Jane made a cake and she made it very sour,
And said, "Dear Jimmy, kiss me every hour."
Janie rode a white horse and Jimmy rode a black.
They rode into Halifax and never did come back.

120 *Somebody, nobody, walks down the aisle*

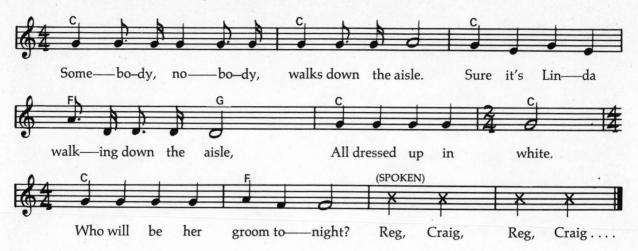

Some—bo—dy, no—bo—dy, walks down the aisle. Sure it's Lin—da

walk—ing down the aisle, All dressed up in white.

(SPOKEN)
Who will be her groom to—night? Reg, Craig, Reg, Craig . . . .

121

A.

Who you gonna marry?
   Tinker, tailor, soldier, sailor,
   Rich man, poor man, beggar man, thief,
   Doctor, lawyer, merchant chief . . .

Where you gonna get married?
   Church, house, barn, pig pen . . .

What you gonna get married in?
   Rags, tags, paper bags . . .

Where you gonna go on your honeymoon?
   Paris, China, London, slums . . .

What you gonna live in?
   House, castle, mansion, pig pen, barn . . .

B.

Mrs. Sippi lives by the shore.
She has children three and four.
The oldest one is twenty-four.
She shall marry:
   Tinker, tailor, soldier, sailor,
   Rich man, poor man, beggar man, thief,
   Doctor, lawyer, Indian chief,
   Royal Canadian Mounted Police . . .

What will she go to the wedding in?
   Jag, Chevy, horse and carriage . . .

What kind of dress will she marry in?
   Silk, satin, cotton batting . . .

What kind of ring will he give her?
   Diamond, ruby, ten-cent ring . . .

What kind of house will she live in?
   Big house, little house, pig pen, barn . . .

At what age will this take place?
   15, 21, 50, never, 15, 21, 50, never . . .

122

Look who's coming down the street:
Nory Martin, ain't she sweet?
She's been married twice before:
Now she's knocking at Henry's door.

Henry, Henry, marry me:
Marry me at half-past three.
Half-past three is much too late:
Marry me at a quarter-past eight.

. . . .

123

Barbara and Tommy sitting in a tree
K-I-S-S-I-N-G.
First comes love, then comes marriage,
Then comes Barbara with a baby carriage.

124

Chungi, mungi,
Chucka chicka chungi,
Alligator ungi, ohhhh!

125 *Yoki and the kaiser*

Yo—ki and the kai——ser, Yo—ki ad—dy ay,

Tam——ba so——ba, Sa—du, sa——day.

A.

Yoki and the kaiser,
Yoki addy ay,
Tam-ba so-ba,
Sa-du, sa-day.

B.

Yoki in the kaiser,
Yoki allee-ay,
Kick him in the so-po,
Sa-du, sa-day.

BALL BOUNCING

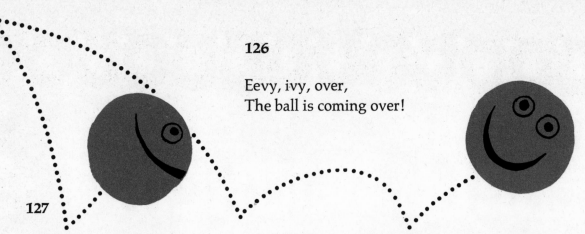

126

Eevy, ivy, over,
The ball is coming over!

127

Gypsy, gypsy, lived in a tent.
She had no money to pay her rent.

She borrowed a one, she borrowed a two,
And passed it on to Y-O-U.

128

Bouncie, bouncie, ballie,
I broke my sister's dollie.
She gave me a whack,
I paid her back,
Bouncie, bouncie, ballie.

129

A.

One, two, three, O'Leary,
Four, five, six, O'Leary,
Seven, eight, nine, O'Leary,
Ten, O'Leary, Postman!

B.

One, two, three, alora,
Four, five, six, alora,
Seven, eight, nine, alora,
Ten, A-Laura Secord!

130 *One, two, three, alary*

One, two, three, a—la—ry, My first name is Mary.

If you think it ne—ces—sa—ry, Look it up in the dic—tion—a—ry.

A.

One, two, three, alary,
My first name is Mary.
If you think it necessary,
Look it up in the dictionary.

C.

One, two, three, alary,
Lost my ball in the city dairy.
If you find it, give it to Mary.
One, two, three, alary.

E.

One, two, three, alary,
I am very merry.
I got a job to carry
Rocks to the cemetery.

B.

One, two, three, alary,
I spy a little fairy
Sitting on a dictionary.
One, two, three, alary.

D.

One, two, three, alary,
I lost my sweet canary.
When you find him, call him Barry.
One, two, three, alary.

F.

One, two, three, alary,
I saw Mrs. Terry
Sitting on a bumbleberry
Eating chocolate candy.

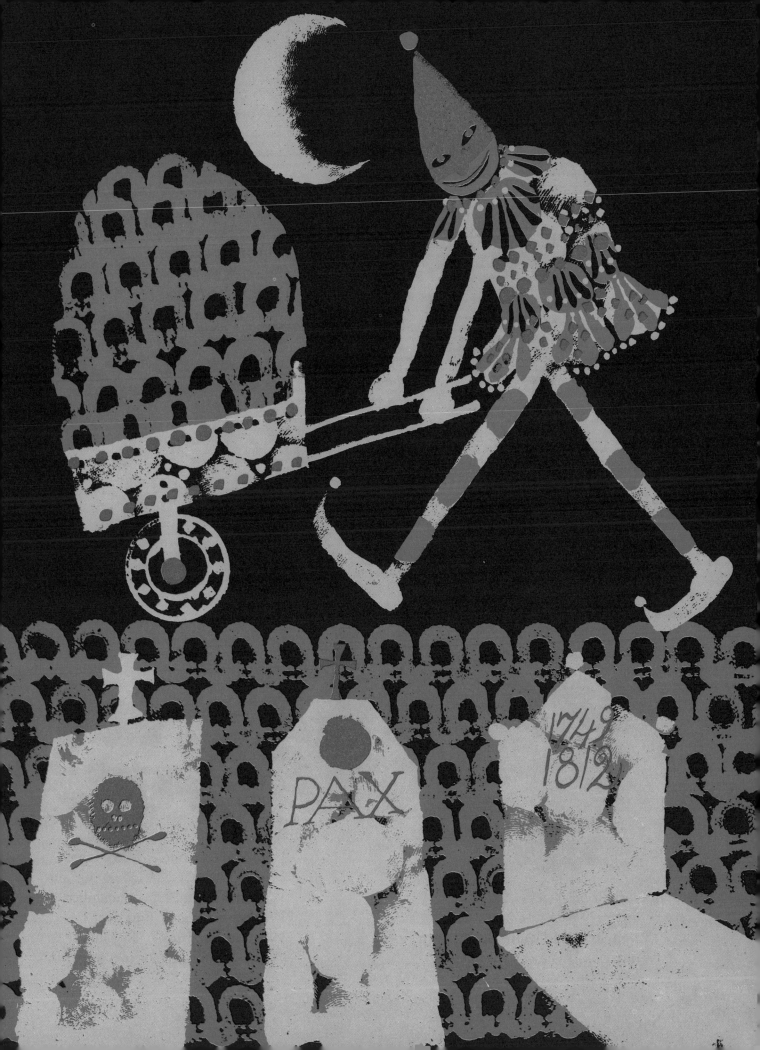

131

One, two, three, bologny.
I had a little pony
And its name was Macaroni.
One, two, three, bologny.

132

One, two, three, a-twirlsy,
Four, five, six, a-twirlsy,
Seven, eight, nine, a-twirlsy,
Ten, a-twirlsy, catch me!

{ Repeat for "a-jumpsy"
{ and "a-crossy."

133

Ordinary clapsies,
Roly poly backsies,
High, low, the heel-toe,
Clip, clop, and away she goes!

134

Ordinary movings,
Laughings, talkings,
One hand, the other hand,
One foot, the other foot.
Clap at the front, clap at the back,
Front and back, back and front.
Tweedles, twaddles,
Curtsies, salutsies,
Bowsies, jumpsies,
And away she goes!

135

Annie Lee, can't you see?
If so, do so.
Touch your knee, touch your toes,
Bounce the ball, and away she goes!

136

What's your name? – Mary Jane.
Where do you live? – Down the lane.
What's the number? – Cucumber.
What do you eat? – Pigs' feet.
What do you drink? – Red ink.
Where do you sleep? – In a jeep.

137

Are you coming out, sir?
No, sir. Why, sir?
Because I've got a cold, sir.
Where'd you get the cold, sir?
At the North Pole, sir.
What were you doing there, sir?
Catching polar bears, sir.
How many did you catch, sir?
One, sir, two, sir, three, sir,
That's enough for me, sir.

140

Help, murder, police!
The teacher fell in the grease.
She laughed so hard she fell in the lard.
Help, murder, police!

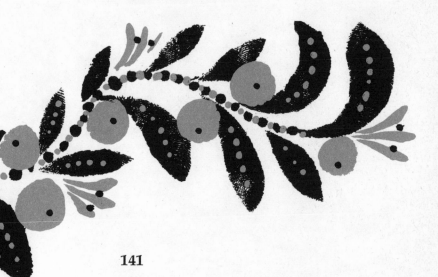

141

Queenie, Queenie, who's got the ball?
Somebody stole it from your home.
Was it John? Was it Jack?
Whoever it was had better give it back.

138

TUNE: REUBEN, REUBEN

I have a dog, his name is Rover.
He is a very intelligent pup.
He will stand upon his hind legs
If you hold his front legs up.

142

A.

The twenty-fourth of May
Is the Queen's birthday.
If you don't give us a holiday
We'll all run away.

B.

Twenty-fourth of May,
Firecracker day!
Kiss the girls, kiss the boys!
Oh, boy, what a joy!

139

Dictation, dictation, dictation,
Two sausages went to the station.
One got lost, the other got squashed,
Dictation, dictation, dictation.

143

Queenie, Queenie, Caroline
Washed her face in turpentine.
Turpentine made it shine,
Queenie, Queenie, Caroline.

144

Tip Top Tailor,
My father was a sailor.
He went to sea and he broke his knee,
Tip Top Tailor!

145

Johnny went over the sea.
Yes, Johnny went over the sea.
He went to visit his grandmother
And when he came back he said to me:
"I jumped aboard a raft
While going over the sea.
The raft tipped over and I fell under
And that was the end of me."

146 *A sailor went to sea*

A sai——lor went to sea To see what he could see And all that he could see Was the deep blue sea.

147

Johnny broke a bottle and he blamed it on me.
I told Ma, Ma told Pa,
Johnny got a licking, and he danced like a chicken,
And he said he wouldn't do it any more.

148 *Elephants marching*

Elephants marching one by one –
Some from the moon and some from the sun.

REFRAIN:
I-O, I-O, I-O, I-O,
I-O, I-O, I-O, I-O.

Elephants marching two by two –
Some for me and some for you.

Elephants marching three by three –
Some for you and some for me.

Elephants marching four by four –
Some through the window and some through the door.

Elephants marching five by five –
Some are dead and some are alive.

Elephants marching six by six –
Some on crutches and some on sticks.

Elephants marching seven by seven –
Some from the moon and some from heaven.

Elephants marching eight by eight –
Some through the window and some through the gate.

Elephants marching nine by nine –
Some are yours and some are mine.

Elephants marching ten by ten –
If you like this song we'll sing it again.

Elephants marching one by one – Some from the moon and some from the sun. I—
O, I—O, I—O, I—O, I—O, I—O, I—O, I—O.

Number One, touch your tongue.
Number Two, touch your shoe.
Number Three, touch your knee.
Number Four, touch the floor.
Number Five, through the hive.

Number Six, do the splits.
Number Seven, up to heaven.
Number Eight, over the gate.
Number Nine, touch your spine.
Number Ten, do it all over again.

150 The ants came marching

The ants came marching one by one, Hur——rah! Hur——rah! The

ants came marching one by one, Hur——rah! Hur——rah! The ants came marching

The ants came marching one by one, Hurrah! Hurrah! (2)
The ants came marching one by one –
The little one stopped to suck his thumb.
They all go marching down around the town.
(Boom, boom, boom.)

The ants came marching two by two, Hurrah! Hurrah! (2)
The ants came marching two by two –
The little one stopped to tie his shoe.
They all go marching down around the town.
(Boom, boom, boom.)

The ants came marching three by three . . .
The little one stopped to climb a tree . . .

one by one – The lit–tle one stopped to suck his thumb. And they all go march—ing

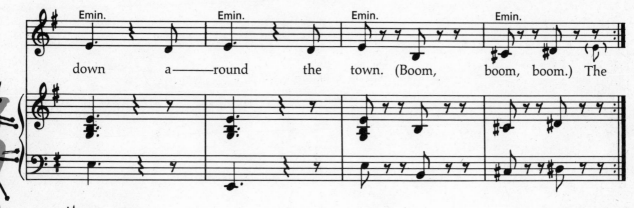

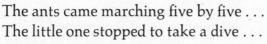

down a———round the town. (Boom, boom, boom.) The

The ants came marching four by four . . .
The little one stopped to shut the door . . .

The ants came marching five by five . . .
The little one stopped to take a dive . . .

The ants came marching six by six . . .
The little one stopped to pick up sticks . . .

The ants came marching seven by seven . . .
The little one stopped to go to heaven . . .

The ants came marching eight by eight . . .
The little one stopped to shut the gate . . .

The ants came marching nine by nine . . .
The little one stopped to scratch his spine . . .

The ants came marching ten by ten . . .
The little one stopped to say THE END.

151 Going over the sea

When I was one, I ate a bun, Go—ing over the sea. I

jumped aboard a Chinaman's ship And the Chinaman said to me: "Go—ing

o—ver, go—ing under, Stand at at—tention like a soldier With a one, two, three."

When I was one, I ate a bun,
Going over the sea. *sailing pirate*
I jumped aboard a Chinaman's ship
And the Chinaman said to me: *captain*
  "Going over, going under,
    Stand at attention like a soldier
    With a one, two, three."

When I was two, I buckled my shoe,
Going over the sea.
I jumped aboard a Chinaman's ship
And the Chinaman said to me:
  "Going over, going under,
    Stand at attention like a soldier
    With a one, two, three."

When I was three, I banged my knee,
Going over the sea . . . .

When I was four, I shut the door,
Going over the sea . . . .

When I was five, I learned to jive,
Going over the sea . . . .

When I was six, I picked up sticks,
Going over the sea . . . .

When I was seven, I went to heaven,
Going over the sea . . . .

When I was eight, I learned to skate,
Going over the sea . . . .

When I was nine, I drank some wine,
Going over the sea . . . .

When I was ten, I strangled a hen, *tickled my*
Going over the sea . . . .

152 *When Buster Brown was one*

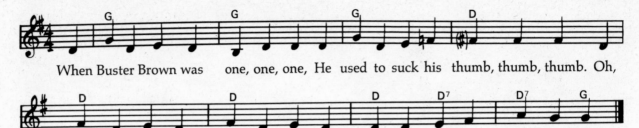

When Buster Brown was one, one, one, He used to suck his thumb, thumb, thumb. Oh, thumb me o—ver, thumb me o—ver, Thumb me o—ver, Bus—ter Brown!

When Buster Brown was one, one, one,
He used to suck his thumb, thumb, thumb.
    Oh, thumb me over, thumb me over,
    Thumb me over, Buster Brown!

When Buster Brown was two, two, two,
He used to tie his shoe, shoe, shoe.
    Oh, shoe me over, shoe me over,
    Shoe me over, Buster Brown!

When Buster Brown was three, three, three,
He used to climb a tree, tree, tree.
    Oh, tree me over, tree me over,
    Tree me over, Buster Brown!

When Buster Brown was four, four, four,
He used to slam the door, door, door . . .

When Buster Brown was five, five, five,
He used to play with a bee hive, hive, hive . . .

When Buster Brown was six, six, six,
He used to play with sticks, sticks, sticks . . .

When Buster Brown was seven, seven, seven,
He almost went to heaven, heaven, heaven . . .

When Buster Brown was eight, eight, eight,
He used to slam the gate, gate, gate . . .

When Buster Brown was nine, nine, nine,
He used to drink the wine, wine, wine . . .

When Buster Brown was ten, ten, ten,
He used to eat the hen, hen, hen . . .

153

A: My name is Anne, and my husband's name is Alex.
We come from Australia and we sell apples.

B: My name is Betty, and my husband's name is Bob.
We come from Brazil and we sell baskets.

C: My name is Corinne and my husband's name is Christopher.
We come from Cork and we sell crayons.

And so on for all the letters of the alphabet.

154

Patty cake, patty cake, baker's man,
Bake me a cake as fast as you can.
Roll it and pat it and mark it with B
And put it in the oven for Baby and me.

155 *I am a pretty little Dutch girl*

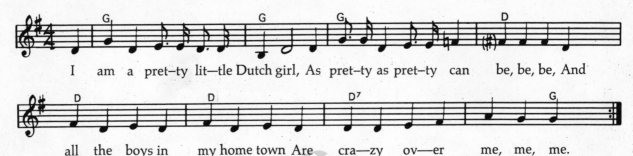

I am a pret-ty lit-tle Dutch girl, As pret-ty as pret-ty can be, be, be, And
all the boys in my home town Are cra-zy ov-er me, me, me.

I am a pretty little Dutch girl,
As pretty as pretty can be, be, be,
And all the boys in my home town
Are crazy over me, me, me.

One day as I was walking
I heard my boy friend talking
To a pretty little girl with a big fat curl
And this is what he said to her:

"I love you oh so dearly,
I love you quite sincerely,
So go away and fly a kite
And everything will be all right."

My boy friend gave me peaches,
My boy friend gave me pears,
My boy friend gave me fifty cents
And kissed me on the stairs.

My mother ate the peaches,
My brother ate the pears,
My father ate the fifty cents
And fell right down the stairs.

My mother called the doctor,
My brother called the nurse,
But all my father really did
Was stay in bed at Gravenhurst.

156

I am a pretty little Dutch girl,
As pretty as can be, be, be,
And all the boys in the baseball team
Are crazy over me, me, me.

I woke up Sunday morning
And looked up on the wall, wall, wall.
The beetles and the bedbugs
Were having a game of ball.

The score was two to nothing –
The beetles were ahead.
The bedbugs knocked a homer
And knocked me out of bed.

157

Old Lady Mack, Mack, Mack,
All dressed in black, black, black,
With silver buttons, buttons, buttons
All down her back, back, back.

I asked my mother, mother, mother
For fifty cents, cents, cents,
To see the elephant, elephant, elephant
Jump the fence, fence, fence.

He jumped so high, high, high
He reached the sky, sky, sky.
He never came back, back, back
Till the end of July, July, July.

158

My boy friend's name was Fatty –
He came from Cincinnati,
With a pimple on his nose and ten fat toes,
And this is how my story goes:

My mother was born in England,
My father was born in France,
And I was born in diapers
Because I had no pants.

159

Pease porridge hot,
Pease porridge cold,
Pease porridge in the pot
Nine days old.

Some like it hot,
Some like it cold,
Some like it in the pot
Nine days old.

Daddy likes it hot,
Mamma likes it cold,
Susy likes it in a pot
Nine days old.

160 Momma, momma, have you heard?

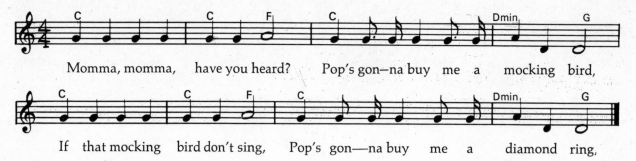

Momma, momma,   have you heard?   Pop's gon—na buy   me   a   mocking   bird,

If   that mocking   bird don't sing,   Pop's gon—na buy   me   a   diamond   ring,

Momma, momma, have you heard?
Pop's gonna buy me a mocking bird,

If that mocking bird don't sing,
Pop's gonna buy me a diamond ring,

If that diamond ring don't shine,
Pop's gonna buy me a bottle of wine,

If that bottle of wine gets broke,
Pop's gonna buy me a billy-goat,

If that billy-goat runs away,
Pop's gonna spank my boomsy-ay,

If my boomsy-ay gets sore,
Pop's gonna buy me a grocery-store,

If that grocery-store burns down,
Pop's gonna buy me an evening gown,

If that evening gown don't fit,
Pop's gonna say, "I quit, quit, quit!"

161

Sing a song of sixpence, a pocket full of rye,
Four and twenty blackbirds baked in a pie.
When the pie was opened, the birds began to sing.
Wasn't that a dainty dish to set before a king?

The king was in his counting-house, counting out his money
The queen was in the parlour, eating bread and honey.
The maid was in the garden, hanging out the clothes:
Along came a blackbird and snapped off her nose.

Her nose began to bleed, like a garden full of seed.
The seed began to grow, like a mountain full of snow.
The snow began to melt, like a ship without a belt.
The ship began to sail, like a bird without a tail.
The bird began to fly, like an eagle in the sky.
The sky began to roar, like a clap upon the door.
The door began to shake, made the paper blue and black.

162 Sandy Dow

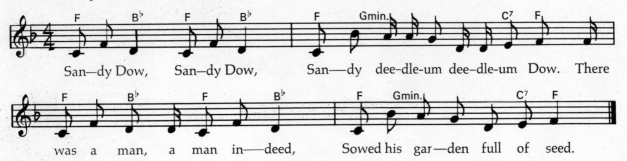

San—dy Dow, San—dy Dow, San—dy dee—dle—um dee—dle—um Dow. There

was a man, a man in—deed, Sowed his gar—den full of seed.

Sandy Dow, Sandy Dow,
Sandy deedle-um deedle-um Dow.

There was a man, a man indeed,
Sowed his garden full of seed.

When the seed began to grow
Like a garden full of snow,

When the snow began to melt
Like a ship without a belt,

When the ship began to sail
Like a bird without a tail,

When the bird began to fly
Like a diamond in the sky,

When the sky began to roar
Like a lion at my door,

When my door began to crack
Like a pain upon my back,

When my back began to break,
Oh, 'twas sore, 'twas sore indeed!

("Dow" is pronounced "doe.")

163 Bingo

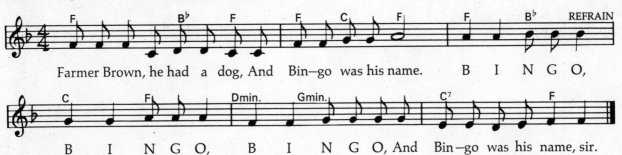

Farmer Brown, he had a dog, And Bin—go was his name. B I N G O,

B I N G O, B I N G O, And Bin—go was his name, sir.

Farmer Brown, he had a dog,
And Bingo was his name.
B-I-N-G-O, B-I-N-G-O, B-I-N-G-O,
And Bingo was his name, sir.

Farmer Brown, he had a dog,
And Bingo was his name.
B-I-N-G (clap), B-I-N-G (clap), B-I-N-G (clap),
And Bingo was his name, sir.

(Repeat, replacing one letter by claps each time.)

164 *Who stole my chickens and my hens?*

165

Zing, zang, zoom, my heart goes ka-boom!
Who stole the cookie from the cookie jar?

Was it you, Number One?
Who, me? – Yes, you.

Couldn't be. – Then who?
Was it you, Number Two?
Who, me? – Yes, you.
Couldn't be. – Then who?
Was it you, Number Three? ...

166

Let's take a W-A-L-K, walk
In the P-A-R-K, park,
And I will K-I-S-S, kiss you
In the D-A-R-K, dark,

And I will L-O-V-E, love you
All the T-I-M-E, time,
And I will never never leave you
For a D-I-M-E, dime.

167

It's raining, it's pouring,
The old man is snoring.
He went to bed with a hole in his head
And he couldn't get up in the morning.

168 *Nobody likes me*

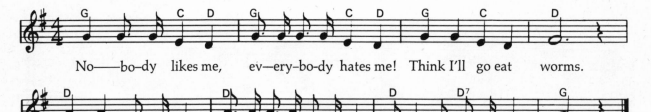

No——bo-dy likes me, ev—ery-bo-dy hates me! Think I'll go eat worms.

Big fat jui—cy ones, eeny-weeny squeemy ones See how they wiggle and squirm.

Nobody likes me, everybody hates me!
Think I'll go eat worms.
Big fat juicy ones, eeny-weeny squeemy ones –
See how they wiggle and squirm.

Chop up their heads and squeeze out their juice,
And throw their tails away.
Nobody knows how I survive
On worms three times a day.

169 Come all you playmates

Come all you play——mates, come out and play with me, And bring your

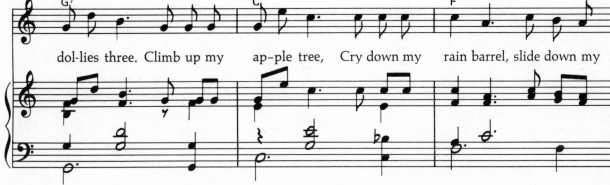

dol-lies three. Climb up my ap-ple tree, Cry down my rain barrel, slide down my

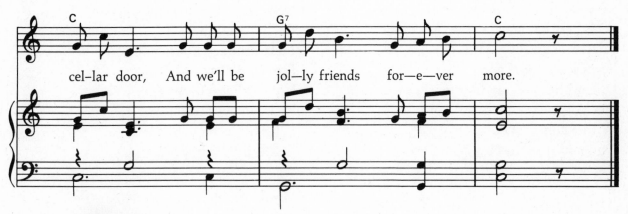

cel-lar door, And we'll be jol—ly friends for—e—ver more.

Come all you playmates, come out and play with me,
And bring your dollies three. Climb up my apple tree,
Cry down my rain barrel, slide down my cellar door,
And we'll be jolly friends forever more.

I'm sorry, playmates, I cannot play with you.
My dolly's got the flu. Boo hoo hoo hoo hoo.
Ain't got no rain barrel, ain't got no cellar door,
But we'll be jolly friends forever more.

170 Down by the bay

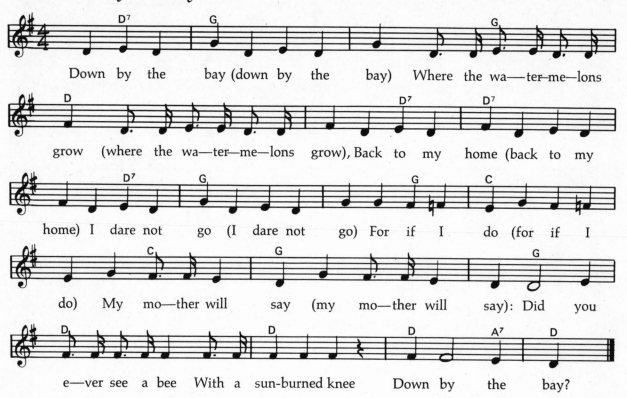

Down by the bay (down by the bay) Where the wa—ter—me—lons grow (where the wa—ter—me—lons grow), Back to my home (back to my home) I dare not go (I dare not go) For if I do (for if I do) My mo—ther will say (my mo—ther will say): Did you e—ver see a bee With a sun-burned knee Down by the bay?

Down by the bay (down by the bay)
Where the watermelons grow
(where the watermelons grow),
Back to my home (back to my home)
I dare not go (I dare not go)
For if I do (for if I do)
My mother will say (my mother will say):
Did you ever see a bee
With a sun-burned knee
Down by the bay?

Down by the bay (down by the bay)
Where the watermelons grow
(where the watermelons grow),
Back to my home (back to my home)
I dare not go (I dare not go)
For if I do (for if I do)
My mother will say (my mother will say):
Did you ever see a cow
With a green eyebrow
Down by the bay?

{ Repeat for "a moose with a loose tooth"
{ and "a witch digging in a ditch."

171

TUNE: LITTLE BROWN JUG

My mother said that I never should
Play with the gypies in the wood.
If I did, she would say:
"Naughty girl to disobey!
Disobey, disobey,
Naughty girl to disobey!"

"Your hair shan't curl, your shoes shan't shine.
You naughty girl, you shan't be mine."
My father said that if I did,
He'd bang my head with a saucepan lid.
Saucepan lid, saucepan lid,
He'd bang my head with a saucepan lid.

The wood was dark, the grass was green.
Up comes Sally with a tambourine.
Alpaca frock, new scarf-shawl,
White straw bonnet and a pink parasol.
Pink parasol, pink parasol,
White straw bonnet and a pink parasol.

I went to the river, no ship to get across.
I paid ten shillings for an old blind horse.
I up on his back and off in a crack.
Sally, tell my mother that I'll never come back.
Never come back, never come back,
Sally, tell my mother that I'll never come back.

• •

172

TUNE: TAKE ME OUT TO THE BALL GAME

Take me out to the hospital,
Take me up to my room.
Give me some needles and I don't care
For I'm in love with Doctor Kildare.
   Oh, it's root toot toot for the nurses:
   If they don't kiss it's a shame,
   For it's one, two, three strikes and out
   At the old hospital.

Take me out to the hospital,
Take me up to my room.
Give me some daisies for I'll be lazy
For I'm in love with Doctor Ben Casey.
   Oh, it's root toot toot for the nurses:
   If they don't kiss, it's a shame,
   For it's one, two, three strikes and out
   At the old hospital.

There were three jolly fishermen. There were three jolly fishermen. Fi—sher, fi—sher, men, men, men! Fi—sher, fi—sher, men, men, men! There were three jolly fishermen!

There were three jolly fishermen...

The first one's name was Abraham...

The second one's name was Isaac...

The third one's name was Jacob...

They all went to Amster... *(cover mouth)*

You shouldn't say that naughty word...

We're going to say it anyway!
We're going to say it anyway!
Amster, Amster, DAM, DAM, DAM!
Amster, Amster, DAM, DAM, DAM!
We're going to say it anyway!

FOOT AND FINGER PLAYS

FOOT PLAY

174

Cobbler, cobbler, mend my shoe.
Give it one stitch; give it two.
Give it three, give it four,
And if it needs it, give it more.

175

This little pig went to market,
This little pig stayed at home,
This little pig had roast beef,
This little pig had none,
This little pig cried "Wee wee wee!"
All the way home.

DANDLING RHYMES

176

Ride a white mare to Banbury Fair
To see what a penny will buy.
A farthing for cake, a farthing for ale,
And a ha'penny apple pie.

177

This is the way the lady rides:
Trit trot, trit trot.

This is the way the gentleman rides:
Jiggety jog, jiggety jog.

This is the way the farmer rides:
Hobbledehoy, hobbledehoy.

This is the way the hunter rides:
Gallupy, gallupy, gallupy over the fence!

178

As I went up yonder hill

I met a fellow fogo

Turning up thumbeline,

Thumbeline a dogo.

I called to Peter Wilson

To fight a fellow fogo,

Turning up a thumbeline,

Thumbeline a dogo.

To market, to market, to buy a fat pig.
Home again, home again, jiggety jig.

To market, to market, to buy a fat hog.
Home again, home again, jiggety jog.

To market, to market, to buy a plum bun.
Home again, home again, marketing's done.

180 Sweetest little baby

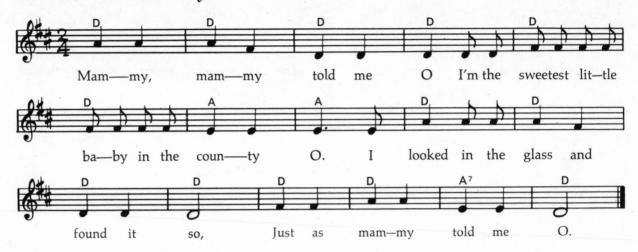

Mam—my,   mam—my   told   me   O   I'm the   sweetest lit—tle
ba—by in the   coun—ty   O.   I   looked in   the   glass   and
found   it   so,   Just   as   mam—my   told   me   O.

Mammy, mammy told me O
I'm the sweetest little baby in the county O.
I looked in the glass and I found it so,
Just as mammy told me O.

Mammy, mammy told me O
You're the dirtiest little rascal in the county O.
I looked in the glass and I found it so,
Just as mammy told me O.

PALM
TICKLES

181

Round and round the cornfield
Looking for a hare.
Where can we find one?
Right up there!

182

Round about, round about
Ran a wee mouse.
Up a bit, up a bit,
In a wee house.

183

Can you keep a secret?
I don't believe you can.
You mustn't laugh, you mustn't cry,
But do the best you can.

FINGER PLAY

184

Here is the church
And here is the steeple.
Open the doors
And see all the people.

See the minister
Mounting the stairs,
And there he is
Saying his prayers.

185

Knock on the door.
Ring the bell.
Peek in the window.
Lift up the latch.
Roll out the red carpet.

186

These are mother's knives and forks,
This is mother's table,
This is mother's looking-glass,
And this is baby's cradle.

187

Put your finger in the crow's nest:
Crow is not at home.
Crow is with the jackdaw
Picking at a bone.

Put your finger in the fox's hole:
Fox is not at home.
Fox came in the back door
Looking for a bone.

188

Two little dickie birds sitting on a wall,
One named Peter, the other named Paul.
Fly away, Peter. Fly away, Paul.
Come back, Peter. Come back, Paul.
Fly away, fly away, fly away, all!

189 TUNE: JOHN BROWN'S BODY

Little Peter *Rabbit* had a *fly* upon his *ear*,
Little Peter *Rabbit* had a *fly* upon his *ear*,
Little Peter *Rabbit* had a *fly* upon his *ear*,
So he *flicked it till it flew away.*

{ Repeat, using actions for "Rabbit" the first time,
"Rabbit" and "fly" the second time, and so on.

190 *Inky pinky 'pider*

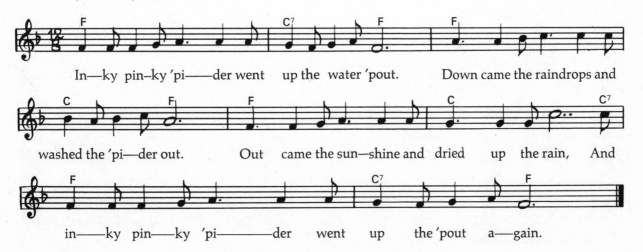

In—ky pin—ky 'pi——der went up the water 'pout. Down came the raindrops and

washed the 'pi—der out. Out came the sun—shine and dried up the rain, And

in——ky pin—ky 'pi——der went up the 'pout a—gain.

191 *Six little ducks*

Six lit—tle ducks that I once knew: Fat ones, skin—ny ones,

they were too, But the one lit—tle duck with the fea—ther on his back,

He ruled the o—thers with his "Quack quack quack! Quack quack quack!"

He ruled the o—thers with his "Quack quack quack!"

* instead of these cords, sometimes let the children
improvise their own "Duck Sounds" on the keyboard

Six little ducks that I once knew:
Fat ones, skinny ones, they were too,
But the one little duck with the feather on his back,
He ruled the others with his "Quack quack quack! Quack quack quack!"
He ruled the others with his "Quack quack quack!"

Down to the water they would go,
Wibble-wobble, wibble wobble, to and fro,
But the one little duck with the feather on his back,
He ruled the others with his "Quack quack quack! Quack quack quack!"
He ruled the others with his "Quack quack quack!"

Home from the water they would come   *(very slowly)*
Wibble-wobble, wibble-wobble, ho ho hum!
But the one little duck with the feather on his back   *(faster)*
He ruled the others with his "Quack quack quack! Quack quack quack!"
He ruled the others with his "Quack quack quack!"

192 *I'm a little teapot*

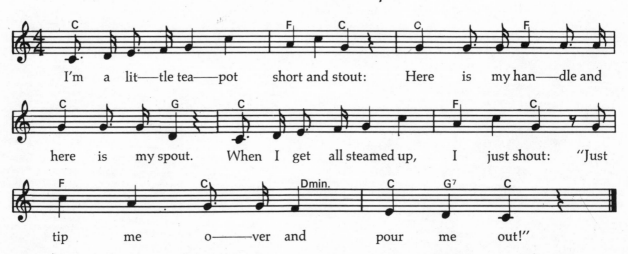

I'm a lit——tle tea——pot short and stout: Here is my han——dle and here is my spout. When I get all steamed up, I just shout: "Just tip me o——ver and pour me out!"

I'm a little teapot short and stout:
Here is my handle and here is my spout.
When I get all steamed up, I just shout:
"Just tip me over and pour me out!"

I'm a very special pot, it's true.
Here's an example of what I can do:
I can turn my handle into a spout.
Just tip me over and pour me out.

COUNTING OUT RHYMES

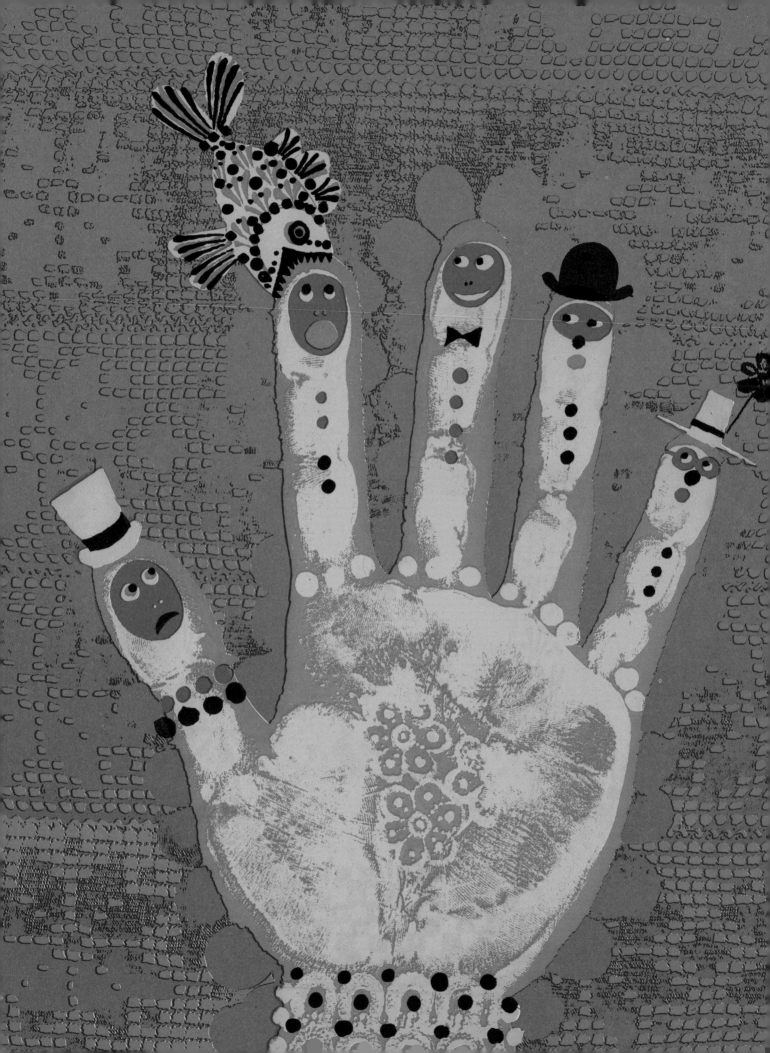

193

One, two, three, four,
Mary at the kitchen door.
Five, six, seven, eight,
Mary at the garden gate.

194

One, two, three, four, five,
I caught a fish alive.
Six, seven, eight, nine, ten,
I let him go again.
Why did you let him go?
Because he bit my finger so.

195

Two, four, six, eight,
Johnny had a rattlesnake.
The snake he died and Johnny cried,
Two, four, six, eight.

196

 One, two, three, four, five, six, seven,
All good children go to heaven.
Those that swear don't go there,
One, two, three, four, five, six, seven.

197

My father had an old horseshoe.
How many nails did he put through?

198

One potato, two potato, three potato, four,
Five potato, six potato, seven potato MORE!

199

Bubble gum, bubble gum in a dish,
How many bubble gums do you wish?
Three. One, two, three, and out you must go
With your mother's big fat toe.

200

Inky, pinky, ponky,
Daddy's bought a donkey.
Donkey died, Daddy cried,
Inky, pinky, ponky.

201

 Eskimo, Eskimo, Eskimo pie,
Turn around and touch the sky.

202

Sky blue, sky blue,
Who's it? Not you.

203

Boy Scout, watch out!
Girl Guide, step aside!

204

Ittle, ottle, bluebottle,
Ittle, ottle, out.

A.

205 Engine, engine number nine
Running on Chicago line,
Running east, running west,
Running through the cuckoo's nest.

A.

206 Ink, mink, who stinks
Like any old mink?
O-U-T spells out
And out you must go.

B.

Ink, ink, a bottle of ink,
The cork fell off and you stink.
Not because you're dirty, not because you're clean,
Just because you kiss the girls behind the magazine!

209 Piggy on the railway picking up stones.
Down came an engine and broke Piggy's bones.
"Oh," cried Piggy, "that's not fair!"
"Oh," cried the engine, "I don't care!"

210 Miss Defoe broke her toe
On the way to Mexico.
Coming back she broke her bac
Sliding down the railway track.

212 Grandfather had some wheat and rye.
He put it out in the barn to dry.
Out came the mice to have some fun.
Up jumped pussy cat and made them all run.

213 Onery twoery ickery Ann,
Fillicy fallacy my son John.
Quebum quavum English knavum,
Stringle-um, strangle-um, BUCK!

214 Onery twoery dickery dee,
Alabo crackabo truder lea.
Twin twan just began,
Twiddle twaddle twenty-one.
O-U-T spells out.

215 Wire, brier, limberlock,
Three geese in a flock.
One flew east and one flew west
And one flew over the cuckoo's nest.

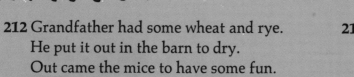

B.

Engine, engine number nine
Running on Chicago line,
At the lake at half-past eight,
Back once more at half-past four.
O-U-T spells out and out goes she!

C.

Engine, engine number nine
Going down Chicago line,
If the train goes off the track,
Do you want your money back?
Yes. Y-E-S spells yes, and out you must go
With a dirty rag tied on your mother's big fat toe.

207 Eeny meeny macker racker,
Rear ride down the racker.
Chicka poppa lollipop,
A rum tum trash.

A.

208 Eeny meeny miny mo,
Catch a monkey by the toe.
If he hollers, let him go,
Eeny, meeny, miny, mo.

B.

Eeny, meeny, miny, mo,
Catch a beatnik by the toe.
If he hollers "Daddy-O,"
Play it cool and let him go.

A.

211 Eeny meeny hippory dick,
Delia dilia dominick,
Ouchy pouchy dominouchy,
Fee fi fo fum,
Ugily bugily boo,
Out goes Y-O-U.

B.

Intry mintry dibbity fig,
Delia, dima, noma, nig,
Hychee, pychee, dominichee,
Gilaba, galaba, goo,
Out goes Y-O-U.

C.

Eeny meeny hipperdick,
Fee fi fo,
Uckle buckle boo,
Out goes you.
Half a peach and half a plum,
Half a pound of chewing gum.

216 Ealy mealy dibbly Dick,
Tine tone Tommy Nick.
Bock nock country brooch,
Tine tone tick.

217 Monkey, monkey, draw the beer.
How many monkeys have we here?
One, two, three – you are he!

218

When I went up an apple tree
All the apples fell on me.
Bake a pudding, bake a pie,
Did you ever tell a lie?
No, I never told a lie
But I ate my mother's sweet apple pie,
With a dirty dish-cloth around her knee.
When this counts out, count one, two, three,
And out goes she!

TAUNTS AND TEASES

STARTING RHYMES

219

One for the money,
Two for the show,
Three to get ready,
And four to go!

220

One to be ready,
Two to be steady,
And three's awa-a-a-ay!

221

One, two, three,
The bumble-bee.
The rooster crows,
And away she goes!

222

Charley on the water,
Charley on the sea,
Charley catch the catbird,
But can't catch me!

223

Ready or not, you must be caught,
Hiding around the goal or not.
Last caught's it!

TAUNTS
AND
TEASES

224

Georgie Porgie pudding and pie
Kissed the girls and made them cry.
When the boys came out to play
Georgie Porgie ran away.

Rosie Posie pudding and pie
Kissed the boys and made them cry.
When the girls came out to play
Rosie Posie ran away.

225

Tattle tale, ginger ale,
Stick your head in a garbage pail.

226

Liar, liar, pants on fire,
Hang you from a telephone wire.

227

Standing on the corner chewing bubble gum,
Along came Nancy and asked for some.
No, you dirty rascal! No, you dirty bum!
You ought to get a licking instead of bubble gum.

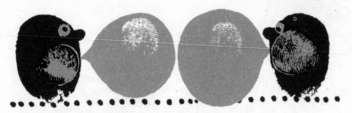

229

My father is a king,
My mother is a queen,
And I'm the little princess,
And you're the dirty thing.
It's not because you're dirty,
It's not because you're clean,
It's just because you've got the whooping cough
And measles in between!

228

There she goes! There she goes!
High-heeled shoes and pointed toes.
Look at her feet! Ain't she sweet!
Black stockings and dirty feet!

230

Tattle tale tit,
Your tongue must be split
And every little puppy dog
Will have a little bit.

234

Kindergarten baby,
Wash your face in gravy.

235

Teeter, totter, bread and water,
Wash your face in dirty water.

236

Up the mountain, down the tree,
You're a bigger fool than me!

237

I'm the king of the castle
And you're the dirty rascal!

232

Little Tommy Tinker
Sat upon a clinker
And he began to cry:
"Maw! Maw!"
Poor little innocent guy!

Little Tommy Tinder
Sat upon a cinder
And he began to cry:
Maw! Maw!"
Poor little innocent guy!

233

Cry, baby, cry!
Stick your finger in your eye.
Tell your mother it wasn't I.

231

TUNE: YANKEE DOODLE

There lived a girl in our street
She's shy and deceitful.
Every little tittle tat
She goes and tells the people
Long nose and ugly face,
Put her in a glass case.
If you want to know her name
Her name is Megan Jenkins.

238

Call me this, call me that,
Call yourself a dirty rat!

239

Sticks and stones will break my bones
But words will never hurt me!

240

Rosy's it. Took a fit.
Couldn't get over it.

241

Cowardy, cowardy, custard!
Had to run from mustard!

242

Fatty, Fatty, two by four,
Couldn't get through the bathroom door!

243

Blue-eyed beauty,
Do your duty.

Brown-eyed brandy,
Eat all the candy.

Green-eyed pickapie,
Turn around and tell a lie.

Grey-eyed greedy gut,
Eat all the world up!

244

Johnny on the woodpile,
Johnny on the fence,
Johnny get your hair cut,
Fifteen cents!

245

I saw you in the orchard,
I saw you in the sea,
I saw you in the bathtub –
Whoops! Pardon me.

246

Anne, Anne, if you're able,
Get your elbows off the table.
This is not a horse's stable
But a ritzy dining table.

247

Mary Jane is no good,
Chop her up for kindling wood.

248

Polly's mad and I'm glad
And I know how to please her:
A bottle of gin to make her grin,
And Johnny Brown to squeeze her!

249

Roses are red, violets are blue,
A face like yours belongs in a zoo.

Roses are red, violets are black,
You'd look better with a knife in your back.

Roses are red, violets are green,
My face is funny, but yours is a scream.

250

Bill the rill, the rick stick still,
The reebo, the ryebo, the scabby-headed Bill.

Jack the rack, the rick stick stack,
The reebo, the ryebo, the scabby-headed Jack.

251

Order in the court house!
The donkey wants to speak.

TRICKS

252

Peter and Paul and Pinch Me
Went down to the beach to bathe.
Peter and Paul were drowned,
And who do you think was saved?
    – Pinch Me.

253

Ice cream and jelly
And a punch in the belly.

254

Here comes a bumble-bee
From behind the barn,
Carrying his bagpipes
Under his arm.
Buzzzzzzz *(poke)*.

TREATS

255 *My Aunt Jane*

My Aunt Jane she called me in, She gave me tea in her wee tin –

Half a bap with sugar on the top, And three black lumps from her wee shop.

My Aunt Jane she called me in,
She gave me tea in her wee tin –
Half a bap with sugar on the top,
And three black lumps from her wee shop.

My Aunt Jane, she's awful smart:
She baked a ring in an apple tart,
And when that Hallowe'en comes round,
Forninst that tart I'm always found.

256

Hippity hop to the barber shop
To buy a stick of candy:
One for me and one for you,
And one for sister Mandy.

257 Watermelons

Just plant a wa—ter—me—lon on my grave And let the

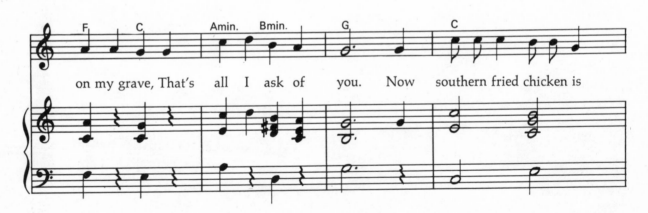

juice (*slu-rup*) slip through! Just plant a wa—ter—me—lon

on my grave, That's all I ask of you. Now southern fried chicken is

258

Open your mouth and shut your eyes
And I'll give you something to make you wise.

migh–ty fine, But all I ask is a me–lon on the vine. Just

plant a wa–ter–me–lon on my grave And let the juice (*slu-rup*) slip through!

259

Fishy, fishy in the brook,
Daddy catch it with a hook,
Mammy fry it in the pan,
Charlie eat it like a man.

260

When you pass the pink ice cream,
Don't act as if you'd like to scream.
Turn your head the other way –
Act like you had it EVERY day.

261

A.

I'll tell you a story about Mother Magory,
And now my story's begun.
I'll tell you another about her brother,
And now my story's done.

B.

I'll tell you a story of Rig-a-ma-rory:
He went to the bush and shot a Tory.
I'll tell you a story about his brother:
He went to the bush and shot another.

262

Nebuchadnezzar, the king of the Jews,
Bought his wife a pair of shoes.
When the shoes began to wear,
Nebuchadnezzar began to swear.

263

Fuzzy Wuzzy was a bear.
Fuzzy Wuzzy had no hair.
Fuzzy Wuzzy wasn't fuzzy,
Was he?

264

Away down south where the bananas grow
A grasshopper stepped on an elephant's toe.
The elephant cried with tears in his eyes,
"Pick on someone your own size."

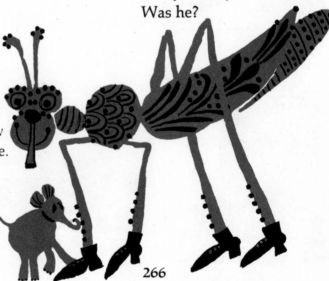

265

A.

There was a little man and he had a little gun,
And the bullets were made of lead, lead, lead.
He came to a brook and he shot a little duck
And he shot it right through the head, head, head.

B.

There was a little man and he had a little gun
And over the mountains he did run,
With a high cocked hat and a belly full of fat
And a pancake tied to his rum-tum-tum.

266

John had some cake;
John had some jelly.
John went to bed
With a pain in his . . .

Now don't get excited –
Don't be misled.
All that John had
Was a pain in his head.

267

A.

Robert and Bobbit and big-bellied Ben
Could eat more meat than four score men;
Could eat a cow and a calf,
An ox and a half,
A church and a steeple,
And all the good people,
And then complain that his belly wasn't full.

B.

Big Belly Ben, four score ten,
Eat more meat than forty men.
Eat a cow, eat a calf,
Eat a butcher and a half.
Eat a church, eat a steeple,
Eat someone, and ALL the people.

268

This is the day they give babies away
With a half a pound of tea.
You open the lid and you find the kid
With a ten-year guarantee.

269

If I were a Cassowary
On the shores of Timbuctoo,
I would eat a missionary,
Skin and bones and hymn-book too.

270

A fly and a flea got caught in a flue,
And then they wondered what they should do.
Said the fly, "Let us flee." Said the flea, "Let us fly."
So they fled through a flaw in the flue.

271

It was midnight on the ocean,
Not a street-car was in sight.
The sun was shining brightly,
And it rained all day that night.

272

Ladies and Jellypots,
I come before you, not behind you,
To tell you something I know nothing about.
I went to the show tomorrow
And took a front seat at the back.
I fell from the floor to the gallery
And hurt the front of my back.
The man at the door was shouting:
"Admission free, pay at the door."

273

As I went up the hoomp-me-shoomp,
The hoomp-me-shoomp-me-sharney,
I met a great big hoomp-me-shoomp
Eating my cabarney.

If I had had my hoomp-me-shoomp,
My hoomp-me-shoomp-me-sharney,
I would have shot that hoomp-me-shoomp
For eating my cabarney.

A horse and a flea and three blind mice
Sat on a curbstone shooting dice.
The horse he slipped and fell on the flea.
"Whoops!" said the flea, "there's a horse on me."

SILLY SONGS

275 Roll over

Ten in the bed, and the lit——tle one said: "Roll o——ver! Roll o——ver!" They all rolled o——ver and one fell out.

Ten in the bed, and the little one said:
"Roll over! Roll over!"
They all rolled over and one fell out.

Nine in the bed and the little one said:
"Roll over! Roll over!"
They all rolled over and one fell out.

Eight in the bed . . .

Seven in the bed . . .

Six in the bed . . .

Five in the bed . . .

Four in the bed . . .

Three in the bed . . .

Two in the bed . . .

One in the bed and the little one said:
(*Spoken*) "Alone at last!"

· ·

276

TUNE: TURKEY IN THE STRAW

Toronto

Oh, I went to Toledo and I walked around the block,
And I walked right into a baker's shop.
And I took two doughnuts out of the grease,
And I handed the lady a five-cent piece.

Oh, she looked at the nickel and she looked at me,
And she said, "This money is no good to me.
There's a hole in the middle and it goes right through."
Says I, "There's a hole in the doughnut, too!"

· ·

277

TUNE: COMING THROUGH THE RYE

Mousie, mousie, little mousie,
Hurry, hurry, do!
Or the pussy in the housie
Will be catching you!

Mousie, mousie, little mousie
Hurry, hurry, do!
Or the pussy in the housie
Will be catching you!

132

278 The baby prune

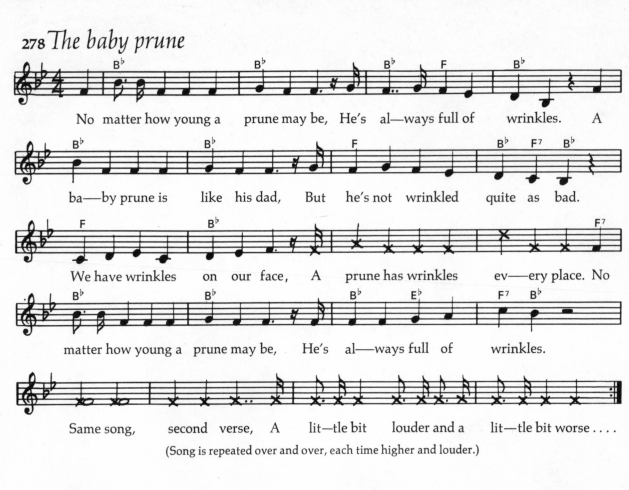

No matter how young a prune may be, He's al—ways full of wrinkles. A

ba—by prune is like his dad, But he's not wrinkled quite as bad.

We have wrinkles on our face, A prune has wrinkles ev—ery place. No

matter how young a prune may be, He's al—ways full of wrinkles.

Same song, second verse, A lit—tle bit louder and a lit—tle bit worse . . . .

(Song is repeated over and over, each time higher and louder.)

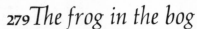

279 The frog in the bog

There once was a frog who lived in a bog And played a fiddle in the

middle of a puddle. What a muddle! Better go round. Better go round.

There once was a frog who lived in a bog
And played a fiddle in the middle of a puddle.
What a muddle! Better go round. Better go round.

His music was short for soon he was caught,
And now in the middle of a griddle he is frying,
And he's crying, "Rather be drowned. Rather be drowned."

134

Yon Yonson

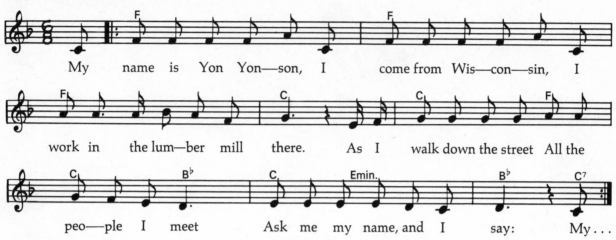

My name is Yon Yon—son, I come from Wis—con—sin, I

work in the lum—ber mill there. As I walk down the street All the

peo—ple I meet Ask me my name, and I say: My...

(Repeat until tired.)

281 *The baby bumble-bee*

I'm bring—ing home a ba—by bum—ble bee: Won't my mummy

be so pleased with me! I'm bring—ing home a ba—by

bum—ble bee: Buzz, buzz, buzz, buzz! Whoops – it stung me!

I'm bringing home a baby bumble-bee:
Won't my mummy be so pleased with me!
I'm bringing home a baby bumble-bee:
Buzz, buzz, buzz, buzz! Whoops – it stung me!

I'm squashing up a baby bumble-bee: I'm eating up a baby bumble-bee:
Won't my mummy be so pleased with me!   Won't my mummy be so pleased with me!
I'm squashing up a baby bumble-bee: I'm eating up a baby bumble-bee:
  Buzz, buzz, buzz, buzz! Ooh – it's gucky!   Buzz, buzz, buzz, buzz! Ooh – my tummy!

282 *I'm a nut*

I'm a little acorn nice and round.
I live away down in the ground,
And ev'ryone walks over me,
And that is why I'm cracked, you see.

REFRAIN:

I'm a nut (click, click), in a rut (click, click)!
I'm a nut (click, click), in a rut (click, click)!

I love me, I think I'm grand –
I sit in the movies and hold my hand.
I put my arm around my waist,
And when I get fresh, I slap my face.

I call myself on the telephone
Just to hear my golden tone.
I ask myself for a little date,
And I pick myself up about half-past eight.

283 The little skunk

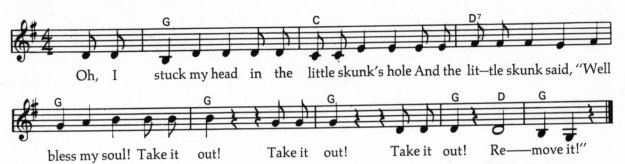

Oh, I stuck my head in the little skunk's hole And the lit—tle skunk said, "Well

bless my soul! Take it out! Take it out! Take it out! Re——move it!"

Oh, I stuck my head in the little skunk's hole
And the little skunk said, "Well bless my soul!
Take it out! Take it out! Take it out! Remove it!"

Oh, I didn't take it out, and the little skunk said:
"If you don't take it out you'll wish you had.
Take it out! Take it out!" Pheeew! I removed it.

284

TUNE: CLEMENTINE

Found a peanut, found a peanut,
Found a peanut last night!
Last night I found a peanut,
Found a peanut last night.

Broke it open, broke it open,
Broke it open last night!
Last night I broke it open,
Broke it open last night.

It was rotten, it was rotten . . .

Ate it anyway, ate it anyway . . .

Got a tummyache, got a tummyache . . .

Called the doctor, called the doctor . . .

Appendicitis, appendicitis . . .

Operation, operation . . .

Died anyway, died anyway . . .

Went to heaven, went to heaven . . .

Didn't want me, didn't want me . . .

Went the other way, went the other way . . .

Wouldn't take me, wouldn't take me . . .

Stayed anyway, stayed anyway . . .

Shovelled coal, shovelled coal . . .

Burnt my thumb, burnt my thumb . . .

It was a dream, it was a dream . . .

285 Banana Bird

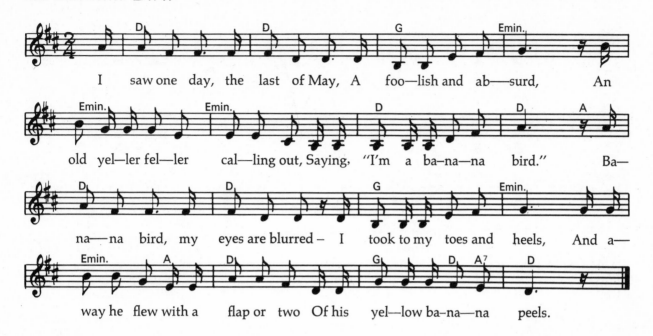

I saw one day, the last of May, A foo—lish and ab—surd, An
old yel—ler fel—ler cal—ling out, Saying, "I'm a ba-na—na bird." Ba—
na—na bird, my eyes are blurred – I took to my toes and heels, And a—
way he flew with a flap or two Of his yel—low ba-na—na peels.

286

TUNE: AULD LANG SYNE

I wish I had a load of rails
To build my fence around
So I could keep the neighbour's pigs
From rooting up my ground.

287

TUNE: *Based on* PUT ON YOUR OLD GREY BONNET

Old Aunt Mariar a-sitting by the fire:
Oh, she wants a drink of gin
Though she knows that it's a sin.
Mariar, Mariar, bay rum in the bottle will buy 'er!
Mariar, Mariar, dirty old Auntie Mariar!

288 Do your ears hang low?

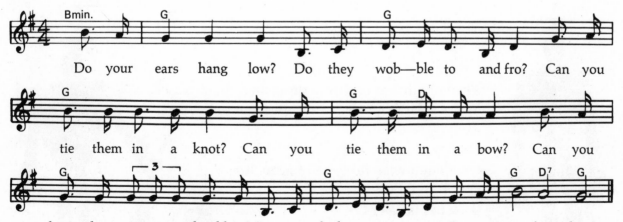

Do your ears hang low? Do they wob—ble to and fro? Can you
tie them in a knot? Can you tie them in a bow? Can you
throw them over your shoulders? Can you pluck a merry tune? Do your ears hang low?

289 *I don't want no more of army life*

They say that in the army the drinks are mighty fine –
You ask for Coca Cola; they give you turpentine.

REFRAIN:

Oh, I don't want no more of army life.
Gee, Mom, I wanta go
Back to On-ta-ri-o!
Gee, Mom, I wanta go home!

They say that in the army the cookies are divine,
But one fell off the table and killed a pal of mine.

They say that in the army the tents are mighty good –
You wake up in the morning and you're floating on the roof.

They say that in the army the boys are mighty fine –
You ask for Ricky Nelson and they give you Frankenstein.

They say that in the army the pay is mighty fine –
They give you fifty dollars and take back forty-nine.

290 *I gave her kisses one*

I gave her kisses one, kisses one.
I gave her kisses one, kisses one.
I gave her kisses one, she said I'd just begun,
So I kept kissing on, kissing on.

I gave her kisses two, kisses two.
I gave her kisses two, kisses two.
I gave her kisses two, she said I wasn't through,
So I kept kissing on, kissing on.

I gave her kisses three, kisses three.
I gave her kisses three, kisses three.
I gave her kisses three, she said she loved me,
So I kept kissing on, kissing on.

I gave her kisses four, kisses four.
I gave her kisses four, kisses four.
I gave her kisses four, she said she wanted more,
So I kept kissing on, kissing on.

I gave her kisses five, kisses five.
I gave her kisses five, kisses five.
I gave her kisses five, she said, "Oh, I am alive!"
So I kept kissing on, kissing on.

I gave her kisses six, kisses six.
I gave her kisses six, kisses six.
I gave her kisses six, she said she'd got the number mixed,
So I kept kissing on, kissing on.

I gave her kisses seven, kisses seven.
I gave her kisses seven, kisses seven.
I gave her kisses seven, she said, "Oh, I am in heaven!"
So I kept kissing on, kissing on.

I gave her kisses eight, kisses eight.
I gave her kisses eight, kisses eight.
I gave her kisses eight, she said, "Oh, it isn't late,"
So I kept kissing on, kissing on.

I gave her kisses nine, kisses nine.
I gave her kisses nine, kisses nine.
I gave her kisses nine, she said she would be mine,
So I kept kissing on, kissing on.

I gave her kisses ten, kisses ten.
I gave her kisses ten, kisses ten.
I gave her kisses ten, she said, "Begin again,"
So I kept kissing on, kissing on.

291

TUNE: THE FARMER IN THE DELL (NO. 5)

I with I wath a fith.
I with I wath a fith.
I'd thwim and thwim the deep blue sea.
I with I wath a fith.

I with I wath a thip.
I with I wath a thip.
I'd thwim and thwim the deep blue sea.
I with I wath a thip.

I with I wath a thafety pin.
I with I wath a thafety pin.
I'd rutht and rutht till everything butht.
I with I wath a thafety pin.

I with I wath thome thlime.
I with I wath thome thlime.
I'd oothe and oothe in everyone'th thoes.
I with I wath thome thlime.

I with I wathn't a thimp.
I with I wathn't a thimp.
I'd thing a thong that had thome thenthe.
I with I wathn't a thimp.

292

TUNE: MY BONNIE LIES OVER THE OCEAN

My body lies over the ocean,
My body lies over the sea.
My body lies over the ocean:
Oh, bring back my body to me!

My body lies over the ocean,
My body lies over the sea.
My body lies out in the graveyard,
And that's where it always will be.

293

TUNE: BYE, BYE, BLACKBIRD

I've lost my underwear.
I don't care, I'll go bare.
Bye, bye, longjohns.
They were very nice to me:
They tickled me.
Bye, bye, longjohns.

294

TUNE: DID YOU EVER SEE A LASSIE? (NO. 13)

Oh, say, John, won't you buy me,
Won't you buy me, won't you buy me,
Oh, say, John, won't you buy me,
Won't you buy me a broom?

A large one for the lady
And a small one for the baby,
Oh, say John, won't you buy me,
Won't you buy me a broom?

295

TUNE: WE THREE KINGS OF ORIENT ARE

We three kings of Orient are,
Tried to smoke a rubber cigar.
It was loaded, it exploded,
And scattered us all afar.

296

TUNE: WHILE SHEPHERDS WATCHED

While shepherds washed their socks by night
All seated round the tub,
A shower of Ivory Flakes came down,
And they began to scrub.

297

TUNE: GOING TO CHICAGO (NO. 20)

Helen had a steamboat. The steamboat had a bell.
Helen went to heaven. The steamboat went to . . .
Hello Operator! Just give me number nine.
If the line is busy, I'll kick you up. . .
Behind the Iron Curtain there was a piece of glass.
Helen stepped upon it and hurt her little . . .
Ask me no more questions, tell me no more lies.
That is the whole story of Helen and her lies.

298

TUNE: HOT TIME IN THE OLD TOWN TONIGHT

Cheer, boys, cheer! The school is burning down.
Cheer, boys, cheer! The school is burning down.
Cheer, boys, cheer! It's burning to the ground.
There'll be a hot time in the old town tonight!

299

TUNE: JOHN BROWN'S BODY

My eyes have seen the glory of the burning of the school.
We've tortured every teacher and we've broken every rule.
We've hid in every corner of the dirty rotten school,
And the class is marching on.

Glory! Glory! How peculiar!
Teacher hit me with a ruler!
I met her at the door with a loaded forty-four
And she's going to teach no more.

300 *I love little Willie*

I love lit—tle Wil—lie, I do, Ma—ma. I
love lit—tle Wil—lie, I do, ha ha! I love lit—tle Wil—lie, but
don't you tell Pa, For he won't like it, you know.

* last verse only

I love little Willie, I do, Mama.
I love little Willie, I do, ha ha!
I love little Willie, but don't you tell Pa,
For he won't like it, you know.

He told me he loved me, he did, Mama.
He told me he loved me, he did, ha ha!
He told me he loved me, but don't you tell Pa,
For he won't like it, you know.

He's gone for the preacher, he has, Mama.
He's gone for the preacher, he has, ha ha!
He's gone for the preacher, but don't you tell Pa,
For he won't like it, you know.

And now we are married, we are, Mama.
And now we are married, we are, ha ha!
And now we are married, so you can tell Pa,
For he can't help it, you know.

Notes, Sources and References

How to play the games

The following section gives brief directions for playing the games, identifies the sources of the particular forms used, and lists a number of comparative references. Many of the items are widely known; some are rare; and a few have not been published before.

The items were collected in Toronto, unless another place is named. Most came from children between the ages of six and ten. For items contributed by adults, the place and approximate date that they learned the verses are given in brackets. Where a school is given as the source, the rhymes came from the Grade III class of the year indicated. Rhymes that form part of my collection in the archives of the National Museum of Canada are indicated by numbers prefixed by FO. A few verses come from a series of weekly articles, "Play Rhymes of the Dominion," that appeared in the Toronto *Globe* between November 13 and December 18, 1909.

Similar rhymes found in other collections are indicated by the names of the collectors whose books or records appear in the bibliography (page 157). When more than one book by the same author is listed, the title is indicated by an abbreviation (i.e., "Wood: *Fun*, 13" refers to page 13 in Ray Wood's *Fun in American Folk Rhymes*). Roman numerals refer to volume numbers, Arabic numerals to page numbers (i.e., "Randolph III, 13" means page 13 in Volume III of Vance Randolph's *Ozark Folksongs*).

Because some of the items appear in scores of books, I have not tried to give complete references, but have cited only the more important collections of children's lore. Wherever possible I have given at least one English and one American source. Additional references will be found in some of the collections listed, notably those of Baring-Gould, Brown, Opie, and Randolph. I have cited rhymes published in magazines only where book references were lacking, and have included a few records of rhymes from traditional sources. In general, the number of references is in proportion to the age and popularity of the rhyme.

Singing Games

1. SALLY GO ROUND THE SUN. Children join hands and circle in a ring, reversing each time they repeat the verse. Gail Hodgins, 1961 (Port Perry, Ontario, 1940s). Cf. Baring-Gould, 251-2; Douglas, 28; Gomme II, 149; Hamilton, TLP 1034.

2. RING AROUND A ROSY. Children circle singing; at end they all sit or fall down. Bruce School, 1962. Cf. Baring-Gould, 253; Brown I, 150; Gomme I, 108; Newell, 127-8; Opie: *Dictionary*, 364; Wood: *Mother Goose*, 102.

3. I WROTE A LETTER. Sometimes called "Drop the Handkerchief." One child walks around the outside of the ring and drops a handkerchief behind someone on "I will bite you." That child chases the first around the ring, and when he catches him takes his place for the next round. Bruce School, 1962. Cf. Baring-Gould, 250; Brown I, 81; Gomme I, 109-12; MacColl, FW 8501; Newell, 168-9.

4. RIG-A-JIG-JIG. Children walk around in circle for verse; on chorus they double the pace. Mrs. Marilyn Rosenberg, 1962, learned in childhood. Cf. Botkin: *Play-Party*, 289-9; Brown I, 128.

5. THE FARMER IN THE DELL. Children circle around one in centre who chooses another, and she in turn chooses another. The last child chosen becomes the "farmer" for the next game. Secord School, 1960 (FO 314). Cf. Brown I, 146; Gomme II, 420; MacColl, FW 8501; Newell, 129.

6. OATS, PEAS, BEANS, AND BARLEY GROW. Children circle around one in centre, imitating the actions described. The one in the ring chooses another, who takes his place for the next round. Mrs. Nancy Takerer, 1963 (Kingston, Ontario, 1940s). Cf. Botkin: *Play-Party*, 254-5; Brown I, 87; Gomme II, 1-13; Holbrook, 81-2; Newell, 80-4.

7. PUNCHINELLO. One child in centre of ring performs some action which the others imitate. Mrs. Marilyn Rosenberg, 1962, learned in childhood. Cf. Sutton-Smith, 30.

8. THE MULBERRY BUSH. Children circle in ring singing first verse (which also serves as a refrain); then they break the ring to imitate the actions mentioned in following verses. Gail Hodgins, 1961 (Port Perry, 1940s). Cf. Baring-Gould, 253; Brown I, 85; Gomme I, 404-7; Holbrook, 90; Newell, 86-7; Sutton-Smith, 19.

9. MONKEY SEE AND MONKEY DO. Same actions as Punchinello. Catharine Potts and Judy Crawford, 1960 (FO 327).

10. ROUND THE MOUNTAIN. Children in pairs circle around one who kneels in the centre. At "Rise, sugar, rise," the kneeling child stands up and chooses another to join him. They make a motion which is imitated by the others. Then the first child joins the circle while the second kneels. Sackville School, 1964. Cf. Brown I, 131.

11. LOOBY LOO. Children dance around in ring singing first verse; then they put a hand or foot into the centre and turn around rapidly on the last line. Alice Kane, 1962, from Toronto children. Cf. Baring-Gould, 252; Brown I, 156; Courlander FC 7004; Gomme I, 352-61; Randolph III, 365-6.

12. HERE STANDS A RED BIRD. Child in centre of ring makes motions which are imitated by the others, and then chooses a partner who replaces him. Sackville School, 1964. Cf. Brown III, 124.

13. DID YOU EVER SEE A LASSIE? Children circle around child in centre for first two lines; then child makes some movement and the others imitate it. Joan, Dick, Beverley, and Janet Louch, Willowdale, Ontario, 1963. Widely known but rarely published. Cf. *Journal of American Folklore* 60 (1947), 34.

14. WHEN I WAS A BABY. Children circle for first two lines of verse, then perform actions suggested by words: putting finger in mouth, pretending to talk on the telephone, etc. As above. Cf. Brown I, 66; III, 20; Emrich, 108; Gomme II, 362-74; Holbrook, 61-3; Newell, 88-9; Sutton-Smith, 19.

15. IN AND OUT THE WINDOW. One child circles outside the ring and then winds in and out under the other children's raised arms. She chooses one who follows her, and then takes her place. Secord School, 1960 (FO 311). Cf. Brown I, 119-22; Gomme II, 122-43; Holbrook, 91-2; Justus, 52-3; Newell, 128-9; Wood: *Mother Goose*, 98.

16. BLUEBIRD, BLUEBIRD. Children form a ring with hands clasped and raised over their heads. One child walks around the ring on the outside and enters under a pair of arched arms. She chooses another who follows her out of the ring and then takes her place. Mrs. Ruth Rubin, New York, 1958 (Montreal, c. 1915). Cf. Courlander, FC 7004; Justus, 44-5; Newell, 118-9.

17. KING WILLIAM WAS KING GEORGE'S SON. Children march around one in centre who points to another and kneels before her. The two kneel together, and when they rise the first kisses the second and takes her place in the circle. Edith Ferguson, 1963 (St. Elmo, Ontario, c. 1915). Cf. Botkin: *Play Party*, 226-7; Brown I, 113-17; Emrich, 180; Gomme I, 302-4; Newell, 73-5, 246-8; Randolph III, 344-9.

18. GREEN GRAVEL. Children join hands and circle. The child named reverses to face the outside, joining hands in that position. The song is repeated until all children are facing out. Rev. W. W. Burnett, Don Mills, Ontario, 1964 (Elora, Ontario, c. 1910). Cf. Baring-Gould, 177; Brown I, 56-7; Douglas, 31; Emrich, 182; Gomme I, 170-83; Holbrook, 63-4; Justus, 54; Newell, 71, 242; Randolph III, 322-3; Wood: *Mother Goose*, 101.

19. RISE, SALLY, RISE. Children circle around girl sitting in centre; she rises and points to another child who joins her in centre; then she joins the ring. Child's name is sometimes used instead of "Sally." A. Mrs. Elizabeth Blair, 1963 (St. Elmo, c. 1900). B. Bruce School, 1962. Cf. FO 270 and 301; Brown I, 130; Gomme II, 149-79, 453-4; Newell, 70; Sutton-Smith, 15-16.

20. GOING TO CHICAGO. Children circle, at first sedately, and then shaking their hips in imitation of vaudeville dancer. Also sung as "We're going to Kentucky." Holy Name School, 1964.

21. OLD ROGER IS DEAD. Also known as "Oliver Cromwell." One child lies on ground while others circle around him, miming the actions suggested by the words. Mrs. Marilyn Rosenberg, 1962, learned in childhood. Cf. Brown I, 46-8; Douglas, 76-7; Gomme II, 16-24; Holbrook, 83-5; Newell, 100; Randolph III, 381-2.

22. THE JOLLY OLD MILLER. Couples march around in a ring with the "miller" in the centre. At "Grab" those on the inside drop their partners' arms and reach for the one in front while the miller tries to get a partner; if he succeeds, the one left out replaces him in the centre. Mrs. Lotys Murrin, 1959 (Kirkland Lake, Ontario, 1940s). Cf. Brown I, 110-13; Gomme I, 289-93; Holbrook, 101; Justus, 51; Newell, 102-3; Sutton-Smith, 27-8.

23. THE PIG IN THE PARLOUR. Couples join hands and circle around the one in the centre. Then they break the ring and circle in a grand chain, giving the right hand to their partner, left to their neighbour, right to the partner, and so on around the circle, grasping right and left hands alternately, with the one in the centre joining in. Then someone shouts, "Change partners," and they pair off, the one left over becoming the "new pig in the parlour." If the first player fails to get a partner, they sing, "The same old pig in the parlour." Sometimes the last line is sung, "And he's an Irishman, too." Mrs. Elizabeth Blair, 1965 (St. Elmo, c. 1905). Cf. Botkin: *Play Party*, 290-3; Brown I, 108-8; III, 113; Randolph III, 305.

24. LONDON BRIDGE. Two children join hands and raise their arms to form an arch, under which the others march. At end they lower their arms to catch one child and ask her to choose between two things previously agreed upon by the leader (i.e., "Diamonds or pearls?"). When she chooses, she stands behind the leader representing that choice. This is repeated until all the children are lined up behind the leaders; then they have a tug-of-war. Secord School, 1960 (FO 304). Cf. Baring-Gould, 254-5; Brown I, 137-40; Gomme I, 333-50; Newell, 204-11; Opie: *Dictionary*, 270-6; Randolph III, 388.

25. THE ROBBERS COMING THROUGH. Played like "London Bridge." Janet Armstrong, Guelph, Ontario, 1957 (c. 1900). Cf. Brown I, 140; Gomme I, 192-9; Holbrook, 102; MacColl, FW 8501; Sutton-Smith, 21-2.

26. ORANGES AND LEMONS. Played like "London Bridge." Louch children, Willowdale, 1963. Cf. Baring-Gould, 253-4; Gomme II, 25-35; Opie: *Dictionary*, 337-9.

27. NUTS IN MAY. Children form two lines facing each other with enough space between so they can march forwards and backwards as they sing the first verse. Then the two children named meet in the centre and try to pull each other over the middle line; the loser joins the winner's side and the game continues until all one side are captured. Merrick Jarrett, 1961, as played by his children. Cf. Brown I, 109-10; Gomme I, 424-33; Holbrook, 99-100; Newell, 89, 236; Randolph III, 373-4 Sutton-Smith, 23-5.

28. JINNY JO. Two children representing Jinny Jo and her mother stand still while the rest form a single line that advances and retreats, singing the verses in dialogue with the mother. Edith Ferguson, 1963 (St. Elmo, c. 1915). Cf. Brown I, 44-6; Daiken, 135; Gomme I, 260-83; Holbrook, 66-7; Newell, 63-6; Sutton-Smith, 18.

29. WE'VE COME FROM SPAIN. Sometimes called "Three Knights" or "Three Lords Out of Spain." Played the same as "Three Kings A-Riding." Mrs. Isabel Wilson, 1963 (Toronto, c. 1915). Cf. Daiken, 83; Evans, 22; Gomme II, 257-79; MacColl, FW 8501; Newell, 39-45.

30. THE ENGLISH SOLDIERS. Two lines advance and retreat in turn as the questions are asked and answered. At "Shoot, bang, fire," the children mime shooting, and then each player takes hold of one on the opposite side and tries to pull him across a centre line. As above. Cf. Brown I, 43 Daiken, 14; Gomme II, 343-60; Newell, 248-9.

31. THREE KINGS A-RIDING. Sometimes sung as "Three Dukes." Three children in one line facing the others advance and withdraw. The child named joins the "three kings" who then become "four kings" for the next round. Lamont Tilden, 1960 (Harriston, Ontario, c. 1920). Cf. Botkin: *Play-Party*, 328-9; Brown I, 89-93; Daiken, 76; Emrich, 178-9; Gomme II, 233-55; Justus, 46-7; Newell, 46-50; Randolph III, 360-1; Sutton-Smith, 25-6.

32. A-HUNTING WE WILL GO. Children march across the room in pairs, separating at the end, one line going right and the other left, back to the other end where they meet and march down the centre together again. Alice Kane, 1962, from Toronto children. Cf. Baring-Gould, 326-7; Gomme I, 243-5; Sutton-Smith, 28.

33. THE GRAND OLD DUKE OF YORK. Children march around in a line; on "when they were up" they stretch tall with hands above head; on "when they were down" they crouch; on "half way up" they walk with knees bent. Also played like "A-Hunting We Will Go," and used as a skipping rhyme. Catharine Potts and Judy Crawford, 1960. Cf. FO 244; Baring-Gould, 138; Brown III, 135; Gomme I, 121; Opie: *Dictionary*, 442-3.

34. THE WHITE SHIP SAILS. Children join hands in continuous line; two at end raise arms while the line, starting at the far end, parades under the arch and then reverses. Also used as skipping chant. Lamont Tilden, 1962 (heard from children in Montreal, 1940s). Cf. FO 251 and 305; Daiken, 153; Douglas, 36; Hamilton, TLP 1034; Ritchie, 27; Sutton-Smith, 24.

35. JIM-A-LONG JOSIE. Players form parallel lines. First couple join hands, raise them up, and side-step down the centre and back. Then they separate, one going right and the other left on the outside of the lines, and the children in each line follow them. When the head couple meet at the foot, they raise their hands in an arch and the other couples go under. The second couple then become head couple and repeat the actions. Mrs. Elizabeth Blair, 1962 (St. Elmo, c. 1905). Cf. Botkin: *Play Party*, 214-16; Randolph III, 385-6.

36. GOING TO BOSTON. Players form parallel lines. Head couple swing in centre, then girl swings with opposite boy, boy with opposite girl, and then together in centre again. They continue on down the line in this way, then join hands and side-step up the line and then down again, taking their place at the foot. Second couple, now the head couple, repeat, and the process goes on until every couple has had a turn. As above. Cf. Botkin: *Play Party*, 148-50; Randolph III, 315-16.

37. MISS POLLY HAD A DOLLY. Children imitate actions suggested by song:

rocking baby, shaking head, putting on hat, carrying bag, knocking at door, giving pill, writing bill, etc. Mrs. Nancy Takerer, from son Derek, 1967.

38. I'M A LITTLE DUTCH GIRL. Boy and girl face each other with hands on hips, doing a little step-toe dance in one spot. In third verse girl motions boy away; in fifth she indicates a necklace by drawing a V-shape on her chest; on last verse the two link arms and swing around. Mrs. Katharine Wyborn, 1963 (near Chatham, Ontario, c. 1948).

39. NO BEARS OUT TONIGHT. Tag game: the one who is it covers his eyes while the others hide, and then goes out to find them, singing this ditty. They growl and chase him, and he tries to reach the goal. Mrs. Kate Hansen, from children in St. John's, Newfoundland, 1965. Cf. Brown I, 81.

40. ONE LITTLE ELEPHANT BALANCING. One child walks carefully along in a straight line; then second, third, and fourth follow until all the children are following the leader. Holy Name School, 1964.

41. IF YOU'RE HAPPY. Children form two lines and perform the actions indicated. Bruce School, 1962.

42. OLD DADDY TOM. Blankets are placed over chairs to form a tent. All the children hide inside except one who walks around the tent and then reaches in to grab the "sheep." *Globe*, December 4, 1909 (Paisley, Ontario). Cf. Gomme II, 375-81; Newell, 117-18.

43. HEAD AND SHOULDERS. Children touch head, shoulders, knees, and toes, clap, and turn around. Lynn Fowke, 1963 (Saskatoon, 1950s). Cf. Schwartz, FC 7003.

44. IT DOESN'T REALLY MATTER. Children follow a leader around in a circle, stretching arms high at "stand tall." Doris Mosdell, 1965 (Toronto, 1920s).

Skipping Rhymes

The largest group of children's rhymes used today are those accompanying skipping. Many of these were originally singing games, counting-out rhymes, or nursery rhymes. As the same verses may be used for skipping, bouncing ball, or clapping, the groupings do not indicate a rigid division, but merely the most popular usage. Often two rhymes are combined, or the same lines incorporated in more than one rhyme.

Many rhymes are associated with a particular skipping pattern, but detailed descriptions would require too much space. Most of them are chanted as two children turn a rope and a third skips. Usually the pattern is suggested by the verse: for example, many mention specific acts which the skipper must perform (turn around, touch the ground, *etc.*) and include some phrase indicating when one skipper runs out and is replaced by another. Many end in a form of counting or repetition where the child continues skipping until she misses.

A reference to "pepper" is the signal for very fast rope-turning, and usually when rhymes end with numbers, the counting marks the beginning of fast skipping. When the rhyme poses a question, the number or word on which the skipper misses is supposed to give the answer. Doing "the splits" means putting one leg over the rope to stop it. In some verses the rope is swung back and forth, not in full circle, until the end of the line, as in "eevy, ivy, over," when it is swung over the head.

45. NOT LAST NIGHT. A. Lenora and Sheila Luscombe and four friends, East York, Ontario, 1959 (FO 241). B. Mrs. Kate Hansen, from boy in St. John's, Newfoundland, 1965. Cf. Brown I, 171; Emrich, 133; Evans, 43; Opie: *Lore*, 23; Seeger, FC 7029; Withers, 34.

46. GIRL GUIDE. Burgess School, 1960 (FO 339). Cf. FO 262; Daiken, 65; Holbrook, 56; Sutton-Smith, 81; Worstell, 35.

47. CINDERELLA. A. Harry Walker, from Ottawa children, 1960. B. P. J. Thomas, from Vancouver children, 1965. C. Mrs. Kate Hansen, from child in St. John's, Newfoundland, 1965. Cf. FO 282; Botkin: *Treasury*, 791; Brown I, 171; Emrich, 130, 133; Evans, 19, 20; Seeger, FC 7029; Sutton-Smith, 80; Withers, 61, 65; Worstell, 4, 17.

48. SPANISH DANCER. This is often combined with other verses. Harry Walker, from Ottawa children, 1960. Cf. Botkin: *Treasury*, 795; Emrich, 131; Evans, 38, 49; Withers, 69; Worstell, 20.

49. TEDDY BEAR. Bruce School, 1962. Cf. FO 333; Botkin: *Treasury*, 791; Daiken, 64; Douglas, 36; Emrich, 130; Evans, 22, 39; Seeger, FC 7029; Sutton-Smith, 81, 82; Withers, 69; Worstell, 21, 27, 42.

50. I HAD A LITTLE TEDDY BEAR. A. East York children, 1959 (FO 238). B.

Louch children, Willowdale, 1963. Cf. FO 287 and 332; Botkin: *Treasury*, 794; Emrich, 136; Evans, 21; Opie: *Lore*, 34; Seeger, FC 7024; Withers, 30.

51. MOTHER, MOTHER. A. East York children, 1959 (FO 240). B. Barry Hall, from Vancouver children, 1962. Cf. FO 240; Botkin: *Treasury*, 797; Emrich, 133; Evans, 26, 50; Hamilton, TLP 1034; Opie: *Lore*, 34; Sutton-Smith, 81; Worstell, 28.

52. JOHNNY'S GOT THE WHOOPING COUGH. Mrs. Isabel Smaller, 1961 (Owen Sound, Ontario, c. 1916). Cf. FO 335; Brown III, 130; Gomme II, 63; Randolph III, 368-9.

53. OLD MAN MOSES. Sackville School, 1964.

54. POLICEMAN, POLICEMAN. Secord School, 1960 (FO 296). Cf. FO 334; Evans, 34; Opie, *Lore*, 236; Schwartz, FC 7003.

55. THERE CAME A GIRL FROM FRANCE. Based on an old English music-hall song, "Knees Up, Mother Brown." East York children, 1959 (FO 233).

56. I WENT DOWN TOWN. East York children, 1959 (FO 263). Cf. Botkin: *Treasury*, 295, 800; Emrich, 134; Evans, 38; Sutton-Smith, 82; Withers, 141; Worstell, 26.

57. THREE CHAIRS. Selwyn School, 1959 (FO 299).

58. MICKEY MOUSE. William Burgess School, 1960 (FO 340). Cf. Opie: *Lore*, 111.

59. BOW WOW WOW. Mrs. Isabel Smaller, from Kathy Haward, 1964.

60. DONALD DUCK. Begins with one child skipping on one foot, then on both feet; then second child joins in, and so on. East York children, 1959 (FO 269). Cf. FO 294; Seeger, FC 7029.

61. ICE CREAM SODA. Mrs. Smaller, from children in Downsview, Ontario, 1962. Cf. Botkin: *Treasury*, 792; Douglas, 27; Emrich, 136; Evans, 10, 33; Gomme II, 202; Opie: *Lore*, 339; Sutton-Smith, 78; Withers, 61; Worstell, 17.

62. BREAD AND BUTTER. John King, from Toronto children, 1962. Cf. Worstell, 5.

63. ALL IN TOGETHER, GIRLS. A. East York children, 1959 (FO 264). B. Lynn Fowke, 1962 (Saskatoon, 1950s). C. Joan Woodland, 1962, learned in childhood. D. Mrs. Mary Jane Young, 1964 (St. Catharines, Ontario, 1940s). Cf. FO 290; Daiken, 71; Douglas, 50; Evans, 17-18; Holbrook, 56; Sutton-Smith, 75; Withers, 60; Worstell, 38.

64. GRAPES ON THE VINE. East York children, 1959 (FO 231).

65. APPLES, PEACHES, PEARS, AND PLUMS. Often combined with other rhymes. Selwyn School, 1959 (FO 291). Cf. Botkin: *Treasury*, 792-4; Daiken, 67, 70.

66. BLUEBELLS, COCKLE-SHELLS. The first two lines are used to introduce various verses. Selwyn School, 1959 (FO 292). Cf. FO 271; Douglas, 53; Emrich, 137; Evans, 19, 51; Seeger, FC 7029 Sutton-Smith, 76; Worstell, 19.

67. MABEL, MABEL. Harry Walker, Ottawa, 1960 (Moncton, New Brunswick, 1930s). Cf. Botkin: *Treasury*, 792; Douglas, 52; Emrich, 134; Evans, 42; Seeger, FC 7029; Withers, 60; Wood: *Fun*, 99; Worstell, 23.

68. PEEL A BANANA. Mrs. Kate Hansen, from Bonnie McGory, St. John's, Newfoundland, 1965. Cf. Seeger, FC 7029.

69. JELLY IN THE BOWL. William Burgess School, 1960 (FO 338). Cf. Evans, 24; MacColl, FW 8501; Withers, 59.

70. TWO LITTLE SAUSAGES. Mrs. Smaller, from Downsview children, 1962.

71. I HAD A LITTLE CHICKEN. Alice Kane, from Toronto child, 1962.

72. POLLY PUT THE KETTLE ON. Selwyn School, 1959 (FO 295). Cf. Botkin: *Play Party*, 293. Newell, 173; Opie, *Dictionary*, 353.

73. ANDY PANDY. Originally a singing game. East York children, 1959 (FO 242). Cf. FO 293; Douglas, 50; Evans, 14; Gomme I, 189; II, 204; Holbrook, 57; Sutton-Smith, 73.

74. MY FATHER WAS A BUTCHER. Harry Walker, Ottawa, 1960, from Simon Yasin who learned it in childhood in Montreal. Cf. Evans, 50; Sutton-Smith, 79; Withers, 20; Worstell, 25.

75. MY FATHER IS A GARBAGE MAN. John King, from Toronto children, 1962.

76. MY MOTHER AND NANCY'S MOTHER. Bruce School, 1962. Cf. Botkin: *Treasury*, 795; Brown I, 168; Evans, 31; Worstell, 22.

77. MY MOTHER AND YOUR MOTHER. Also used for counting out. Stella Roode, 1961 (Montreal, 1940s). Cf FO 274; Brown I, 166; Evans, 31; Schwartz, FC 7703; Seeger, FC 7029; Withers, 85; Wood, *Fun*, 88; Worstell, 22.

78. VOTE, VOTE, VOTE. Selwyn School, 1959 (FO 286). Cf. FO 303; Daiken, 69; Douglas, 32; Evans, 47; MacColl, FW 8501; Opie: *Lore*, 348.

79. SOMEBODY'S UNDER THE BED. Selwyn School, 1959 (FO 285). Cf. Daiken, 63.

80. HERE COMES TEACHER. Harry Walker, from Ottawa children, 1960. Cf. Evans, 51; Seeger, FC 7029; Worstell, 16.

81. TEACHER, TEACHER. Turners ask questions; skippers reply while jumping. Mrs. Nellie Webb, from children in Don Mills, Ontario, 1962.

82. MR. GREEN IS A VERY NICE MAN. As above. Brown I, 179; Daiken, 70; Evans, 51; Opie: *Dictionary*, 168; *Lore*, 364; Sutton-Smith, 39; Worstell, 19.

83. SITTING IN THE SCHOOL-ROOM. Mrs. Smaller, from Downsview children, 1962.

84. DANCING DOLLY. Mrs. W. H. T. Baillie, from daughter, Toronto, 1940s. Cf. Daiken, 63; Douglas, 28; Gomme II, 203; Hamilton, TLP 1034; Holbrook, 56; Ritchie, 110; Sutton-Smith, 80; Wood: *Fun*, 3.

85. TWO IN A HAMMOCK. Usually an autograph album rhyme. Harry Walker, from Ottawa children, 1960.

86. TWO LITTLE CARS. Usually an autograph album rhyme. Mrs. Smaller, from Downsview children, 1964.

87. COWBOY JOE. Selwyn School, 1959 (FO 288). Cf. FO 234; Baring-Gould, 298; Brown I, 184; Ritchie, 33; Withers, 28; Wood: *Fun*, 106.

88. NINE O'CLOCK IS STRIKING. Harry Walker, Ottawa, 1960 (Moncton, N.B. 1930s). Cf. Botkin: *Treasury*, 792; Daiken, 38; Douglas, 38; Evans, 40; Ritchie, 97.

89. HOUSE TO LET. A. Alice Kane, from Toronto children, 1962. B. Margaret Bagshaw, from nieces, 1962. Cf. Botkin: *Treasury*, 793; Daiken, 64; Douglas, 51; Emrich, 136; MacColl, FW 8501; Opie: *Lore*, 12; Ritchie, 20; Sutton-Smith, 73; Withers, 60; Worstell, 29.

90. AS I WAS IN THE KITCHEN. Harry Walker, from Ottawa children, 1960. Cf. Daiken, 63; Douglas, 37; Evans, 34; Holbrook, 57.

91. MISS MONROE. Barry Hall, from Vancouver children, 1962. Cf. Botkin: *Treasury*, 795; Emrich, 110; Wood: *Fun*, 106.

92. THE KING AND THE QUEEN. Selwyn School, 1969 (FO 289). Cf. Ritchie, 27.

93. OLD MOTHER WITCH. Mrs. Smaller, 1963 (Owen Sound, c. 1916). Cf. Evans, 43.

94. DIE, DIE, LITTLE DOG, DIE. Used as opposite of "pepper" in skipping. Also used on swing when it is slowing down. Alice Kane, 1963, from mother, then 84. Cf. Holbrook, 108.

95. YANKEE DOODLE. East York children, 1959 (FO 249). Cf. Ritchie, 13.

96. CHARLIE CHAPLIN. Harry Walker, from Ottawa children, 1960. Cf. Brown I, 172; Daiken, 34; Emrich, 132; Evans, 33, 37; Holbrook, 57; Opie: *Lore*, 110; Sutton-Smith, 82; Withers, 65.

97. FUNNY BOB HOPE. Barry Hall, from Vancouver children, 1959.

98. JILL HAD AN EAR-ACHE. Bruce School, 1962. Cf. Withers, 29.

99. FUDGE, FUDGE. Selwyn School, 1959 (FO 278). Cf. Botkin: *Treasury*, 794; Em-rich, 132; Evans, 44; Seeger, FC 7029; Withers, 64; Worstell, 14.

100. ALOUETTE-A. Boy at Bruce School, 1962.

101. DOWN IN CZECHOSLOVAKY. Selwyn School, 1959.

102. I HAD A LITTLE DUTCH CAR. A. Secord School, 1960. B. Harry Walker, from Ottawa children, 1960. C. Jennifer Hall, from Heidi Strong, Vancouver, 1959.

103. MAGGIE AND JIGGS. Mrs. Nellie Webb, 1962 (Sarnia, 1930s).

104. BLONDIE AND DAGWOOD. Harry Walker, from Ottawa children, 1960. Cf. Botkin: *Treasury*, 802; Emrich, 136.

105. SALAMI. Originally "Salome." P. J. Thomas, from Cathy McAuley, Vancouver, 1964. Cf. Evans, 51; Opie: *Lore*, 38.

106. I'M POPEYE, THE SAILOR MAN. Alice Kane, from children at Cobourg, Ontario, 1963. Cf. Opie: *Lore*, 112; Ritchie, 35.

107. TILLIE THE TOILER. Harry Walker, from Ottawa children, 1960. Cf. Worstell, 21.

108. I LOVE COFFEE. Mrs. Smaller, 1962 (Owen Sound, c. 1916). Cf. Baring-Gould, 250; Botkin: *Treasury*, 791; Brown III, 128; Daiken, 33; Emrich, 131; Evans, 22, 37; Justus, 38; Opie: *Lore*, 117, 385; Sutton-Smith, 79; Withers, 63; Worstell, 4.

109. LORD NELSON. Harry Walker, from Ottawa children, 1960.

110. CHRISTOPHER COLUMBUS SAILED THE SEA. Elizabeth Elms, 1960 (FO 276).

111. CHRISTOPHER COLUMBUS. Mrs. Smaller, from Downsview children, 1962. Cf. Baring-Gould, 180; Evans, 27.

112. OLD MAN DAISY. John King, from Toronto children, 1962. Cf. Botkin: *Treasury*, 793; Evans, 37; Withers, 61; Worstell, 7.

113. HI, RICKY NELSON. Alice Kane, from Toronto children, 1962. Cf. Opie: *Lore*, 116; Ritchie, 49.

114. THE WIND, THE WIND. Formerly a ring game. A. Secord School, 1960 (FO 309). B. Mrs. Smaller, from Downsview children, 1962. Cf. Daiken, 61; Evans, 27; Gomme II, 387; MacColl, FW 8501.

115. ON A MOUNTAIN. Formerly a ring game. East York children, 1959 (FO 254). Cf. FO 283 and 310; Botkin: *Treasury*, 801; Douglas, 49; Evans, 34; Gomme I, 320; Schwartz, FC 7003.

116. DOCTOR, DOCTOR. Formerly a ring game. Helen Kirkup, 1959 (FO 228). Cf. Brown I, 177; Newell, 99.

117. DOWN IN THE VALLEY. Formerly a ring game. Selwyn School, 1959 (FO 284). Cf. FO 245 and 302; Botkin: *Treasury*, 792; Daiken, 81; Douglas, 32, 53; Emrich, 129; Evans, 36; Gomme I, 99; II, 416; Opie: *Lore*, 364; Seeger, FC 7029; Worstell, 1.

118. ROSY APPLE, LEMON, AND PEAR. Formerly a ring game. Bruce School, 1962. Cf. Daiken, 80, 160; Douglas, 35; Evans, 19; Gomme II, 117; Holbrook, 92-3.

119. ALL THE BOYS IN OUR TOWN. Formerly a ring game. Selwyn School, 1959 (FO 297). Cf. Douglas, 32; Gomme I, 2; Holbrook, 94-5.

120. SOMEBODY, NOBODY, WALKS DOWN THE AISLE. William Burgess School, 1960 (FO 330).

121. WHO YOU GONNA MARRY? Divination rituals like these are often combined with other introductory verses. A. Harry Walker, from Ottawa children, 1960. B. P. J. Thomas, from Vancouver children, 1964. Cf. FO 277 and 337; Daiken, 64, 67; Emrich, 134; Evans, 24-6; Newell, 105-6; Seeger, FC 7029; Withers, 62; Worstell, 18.

122. LOOK WHO'S COMING DOWN THE STREET. Sackville School, 1962.

123. BARBARA AND TOMMY. Usually an autograph album rhyme. Sheila Luscombe, 1959 (FO 257). Cf. Western Folklore XX (1961), 180.

124. CHUNGI MUNGI. Selwyn School, 1959 (FO 281).

125. YOKI AND THE KAISER. This rhyme, in many forms, is very popular with Canadian children. It is used for a variation on skipping in which a long piece of elastic is raised and lowered while the player goes over or under it. It is said to be a Korean children's game that the children of missionaries brought back to Canada. Margaret Burbidge, daughter of Rev. and Mrs. W. A. Burbidge, came home to Toronto from Korea in 1939 and introduced the game into

Humewood public school. She says the original words in phonetic spelling were:

Riojun Kaijo Yaku naride
Deki no syo-koong Stetseru
Noki daisye-do Kai Ken no
Do Ko ro was Isko sui si ei,

and gives this rough translation: "After the agreement to open the gate of the castle (or stronghold) the place where General Nogi met General Stetseru, the general of the enemy was at Shi Ei." That was the battle for possession of Port Arthur in the Russo-Japanese War of 1905, and a Japanese poet wrote a song to celebrate it. After that war, the Japanese occupied Korea, and this song was taught to commemorate the victory, and picked up by children for their game. It is now widely known throughout Canada, usually as "Yoki and the Kaiser." A. East York children, 1959 (FO 232). B. Elizabeth Elms, 1960. Cf. Maclean's, July 6, 1963, 18, 42.

Ball Bouncing

Some ball-bouncing rhymes are used when throwing a ball over a wall or building, and some when bouncing the ball against a wall. More common are the rhymes used to emphasize the rhythm in bouncing the ball on the floor. Sometimes the children bounce their own balls; sometimes they pass them from one to another. As in skipping, many of their rhymes indicate actions to be taken while they bounce, and in some repeated words are signals to pass the leg over the ball: for example, "sir" in "Are You Coming Out, Sir?" (No. 137) and "sea" or "see" in "A Sailor Went to Sea" (No. 146), and "O'Leary" or "Alary" in Nos. 129 and 130.

126. EEVY IVY OVER. Elizabeth Elms, 1960. Cf. Evans, 19.

127. GYPSY, GYPSY. East York children, 1959 (FO 248). Cf. Emrich, 138; Schwartz, FC 7003; Withers, 64.

128. BOUNCIE, BOUNCIE, BALLIE. Mrs. Mary Jane Young, 1963 (Owen Sound, 1940s). Cf. Botkin: *Treasury*, 797.

129. ONE, TWO, THREE, O'LEARY. A. Mrs. W. T. H. Baillie, from daughter, Toronto, 1930s. B. East York children, 1959 (FO 250). Cf. Daiken, 33; Emrich, 138; MacColl, FW 8501; Sutton-Smith, 87; Worstell, 32.

130. ONE, TWO, THREE, ALARY. A. East York children, 1959 (FO 261). B. Mrs. Smaller, from Downsview children, 1962. C. Selwyn School, 1959 (FO 279). D. Mrs. Robertson, heard in Shelburne, N.S., 1964. E. D. C. McCausland, 1963 (Grimsby, Ontario, 1940s). Cf. Daiken, 33; Evans, 46; Ritchie, 37; Withers, 51.

131. ONE, TWO, THREE, BOLOGNY. Mrs. W. T. H. Baillie, from daughter, Toronto, 1930s.

132. ONE, TWO, THREE, A-TWIRLSY. Mrs. Robertson, heard in Shelburne, N.S., 1964.

133. ORDINARY CLAPSIES. East York children, 1959 (FO 267).

134. ORDINARY MOVINGS. East York children, 1959 (FO 268).

135. ANNIE LEE. Sackville School, 1964.

136. WHAT'S YOUR NAME? Alice Kane, from Toronto children, 1962. Cf. FO 272; Brown I, 195; Emrich, 103; MacColl, FW 8501; Opie: *Lore*, 156.

137. ARE YOU COMING OUT, SIR? Very popular. Also used for skipping. East York children, 1959. Cf. FO 280 and 318; Daiken, 33; Emrich, 136; Evans, 40; MacColl, FW 8501; Withers, 62.

138. I HAVE A DOG. Mrs. Katherine Wyborn, 1963 (near Chatham, Ontario, c. 1948).

139. DICTATION, DICTATION, DICTATION. Mrs. Smaller, from Rosemary Ricker, 1964. Cf. Opie: *Lore*, 115.

140. HELP, MURDER, POLICE. Mrs. Smaller, from Downsview children, 1964. Cf. Ritchie, 20.

141. QUEENIE, QUEENIE, WHO'S GOT THE BALL? Mrs. Smaller, from Downsview children, 1962. Cf. Sutton-Smith, 51.

142. THE TWENTY-FOURTH OF MAY. As above. Cf. Opie: *Lore*, 263; Ritchie, 18; Sutton-Smith, 51.

143. QUEENIE, QUEENIE, CAROLINE. *Globe*, Dec. 18, 1909 (Toronto). Cf. Opie: *Lore*, 20, 21.

144. TIP TOP TAILOR. East York children, 1959 (FO 237).

145. JOHNNY WENT OVER THE SEA. East York children, 1959 (FO 236).

146. A SAILOR WENT TO SEA. Barry Hall, from Vancouver children, 1962. Cf. Withers, 52.

147. JOHNNY BROKE A BOTTLE. Also used for skipping. Sheila Luscombe, 1959 (FO 239). Cf. Botkin: *Treasury*, 791, 795; Emrich, 131; Evans, 45; Seeger, FC 7029; Withers, 67; Worstell, 39.

148. ELEPHANTS MARCHING. Louch children, Willowdale, 1963.

149. NUMBER ONE, TOUCH YOUR TONGUE. Mrs. Smaller, from Cindy Schay, Downsview, 1964.

150. THE ANTS CAME MARCHING. Sackville School, 1964.

151. GOING OVER THE SEA. This is very popular in Ontario but does not seem to have been reported elsewhere. East York children, 1959 (FO 235). Cf. FO 300 and 312.

152. BUSTER BROWN. Secord School, 1960 (FO 315). Cf. Botkin: *Treasury*, 801; Emrich, 142-3; Schwartz, FC 7003; Withers, 70.

153. A: MY NAME IS ANNE. This alphabet rigmarole varies with the ingenuity of the children. Also used for skipping. Mrs. Smaller, from Downsview children, 1962. Cf. Emrich, 140; Withers, 54; Worstell, 40.

Clapping Games and Songs

The rhymes used for clapping vary greatly, from old and simple ones like "Patty Cake, Patty Cake" and "Pease Porridge Hot" to more recent and more complicated ones like "Who Stole the Cookie from the Cookie Jar?" and "Who Stole my Chickens and My Hens?" Those are specifically linked with clapping, but many more general songs have been adopted by children for this purpose.

Specific clapping rhymes seem to have a fairly rigid pattern, but when more general songs are used, the pattern is usually improvised, and is more or less complicated depending upon the skill of the clappers. The most common actions include slapping the hands together, slapping the knees, and slapping the hands of a partner.

154. PATTY CAKE, PATTY CAKE. Mrs. Smaller, from Downsview children, 1962. Cf. Baring-Gould, 239; Botkin: *Treasury*, 786; Brown I, 198; Opie: *Dictionary*, 341.

155. I AM A PRETTY LITTLE DUTCH GIRL. Catharine Potts and Judy Crawford, 1960 (Prestige/International INT 25014). Cf. FO 316; Ritchie, 98; Schwartz, FC 7003; Withers, 3.

156. I AM A PRETTY LITTLE DUTCH GIRL. Bruce School, 1962. Cf. Evans, 28; Worstell, 8.

157. OLD LADY MACK. Formerly a ring game. Holy Name School, 1964. Cf. Courlander, FC 7004; Daiken, 65; Evans, 19.

158. MY BOY FRIEND'S NAME WAS FATTY. Burgess School, 1960 (FO 331).

159. PEASE PORRIDGE HOT. Mrs. Smaller, 1962 (from father, Owen Sound, c. 1915). Cf. Baring-Gould, 237; Botkin: *Treasury*, 787; Brown I, 152, 198-9; Newell, 132; Opie: *Dictionary*, 345; Schwartz, FC 7003; Sutton-Smith, 85.

160. MOMMA, MOMMA, HAVE YOU HEARD? Catharine Potts and Judy Crawford, 1960 (FO 323). Cf. Randolph III, 50-1; Withers, 144; Wood: *Mother Goose*, 63-5.

161. SING A SONG OF SIXPENCE. Mrs. Smaller, from Miss Alice McNair, Brampton, 1964 (learned from grandmother, Richmond Hill, Ontario, c. 1900).

162. SANDY DOW. Mrs. Webb, 1962 (from father, Wallacetown, Ontario, 1930s). Cf. Baring-Gould, 81; Brown I, 202-3; Hamilton, TLP 1034; Opie: *Dictionary*, 286-7.

163. BINGO. Formerly a singing game. Louch children, Willowdale, 1963. Cf. Brown I, 154-5; III, 187; Gomme I, 29-33; Sutton-Smith, 20-1.

164. WHO STOLE MY CHICKENS AND MY HENS? Lamont Tilden, 1962 (from children in Montreal, 1940s).

165. WHO STOLE THE COOKIE? Formerly a game called "Who Stole the Cardinal's Hat?" Secord School, 1960 (FO 317). Cf. Brown I, 69; Gomme II, 79; Newell, 145-6; Schwartz, FC 7003.

166. LET'S TAKE A W-A-L-K. A fragment from a popular song very popular with Toronto children. Holy Name School, 1964.

167. IT'S RAINING, IT'S POURING. East York children, 1959 (FO 266). Cf. Baring-Gould, 322; Opie: *Lore*, 218; Sutton-Smith, 99; Withers, 47.

168. NOBODY LIKES ME. Secord School, 1960 (FO 307). Cf. Opie: *Lore*, 175.

169. COME ALL YOU PLAYMATES. Also sung as "Come All You Campers" and "Come All You Brownies." Based on a popular song of 1894: H. W. Petrie's "I Don't Want to Play in Your Yard." Louch children, Willowdale, 1963.

170. DOWN BY THE BAY. This song was popular with soldiers of World War I (*Songs and Slang of the British Soldier*, 1914-1918, by John Brophy and Eric Partridge, London: Eric Partridge Ltd., 1930, p. 34). Holy Name School, 1964.

171. MY MOTHER SAID. Mrs. Donald Ewing, Burlington, Ontario, 1957 (Toronto, 1930s). Cf. Baring-Gould, 240; Daiken, 158; Opie: *Dictionary*, 315; Sutton-Smith, 85.

172. TAKE ME OUT TO THE HOSPITAL. Bruce School, 1962.

173. THREE JOLLY FISHERMEN. Kevin MacMillan, 1967.

Foot and Finger Plays

Most of the rhymes in this book are the kind that children learn from other children without benefit of adults, but those used for foot and finger games are usually heard first from adults, although they may later circulate among the children themselves.

This group includes the foot-patting and dandling rhymes used with very young children, foot-riding and palm-tickling games used with slightly older ones, and a number of finger-play rituals and action songs. Most of them are of considerable antiquity.

174. COBBLER, COBBLER, MEND MY SHOE. Foot patting rhyme. Mrs. Webb, 1964 (Sarnia, 1930s). Cf. Baring-Gould, 235; Opie: *Dictionary*, 125.

175. THIS LITTLE PIG. The child's toes are pulled in turn, from the big toe to the little one. Heard in Saskatchewan in the 1920s. Cf. Baring-Gould, 233; Botkin: *Treasury*, 783; Brown I, 186; Opie: *Dictionary*, 349-50; Sutton-Smith, 134; Withers, 109.

176. RIDE A WHITE MARE. For bouncing child on knee or on foot. Mrs. Webb, 1967 (learned from mother, Sarnia, 1930s). Cf. Baring-Gould, 246-7; Opie: *Dictionary*, 67.

177. THIS IS THE WAY THE LADY RIDES. Eleanor Kelly, 1964 (learned in 1920s from father who came from Guelph). Cf. Baring-Gould, 230; Opie: *Dictionary*, 257-8.

178. AS I WENT UP YONDER HILL. Mrs. Webb, from Phyllis M. Stevenson, Prescott, Ontario, who learned it from her father.

179. TO MARKET, TO MARKET. Mrs. Smaller, from Downsview children, 1962. Cf. Baring-Gould, 230; Opie: *Dictionary*, 299.

180. SWEETEST LITTLE BABY. Dandling song or lullaby. Alice Kane, 1963 (Belfast, c. 1915).

181. ROUND AND ROUND THE CORNFIELD. On last line finger creeps up arm and hair is gently tugged. Mrs. Webb, 1963 (Sarnia, 1930s).

182. ROUND ABOUT, ROUND ABOUT. On last two lines hand goes up arm and tickles under the arm. Mrs. Webb, 1967, from Scottish aunt.

183. CAN YOU KEEP A SECRET? Child's palm is circled with forefinger. Mrs. Webb, 1967, learned from English grandmother and used with her own children.

184. HERE IS THE CHURCH. A finger-locking game. Fingers are intertwined inside hands to form church roof; two forefingers are raised for the steeple; the hands are turned inside out to show fingers for people. For preacher going upstairs, fingers are intertwined facing out, starting with the little fingers; then turn hand so that wrists are crossed and one thumb crosses the other, which is wrig-

gled. Mrs. Webb, 1967 (Sarnia, 1930s). Cf. Baring-Gould, 240; Botkin: *Treasury*, 789; Brown I, 187; Daiken, 142; Newell, 138; Opie: *Dictionary*, 125; Sutton-Smith, 133; Withers, 108; Wood: *Mother Goose*, 107.

185. KNOCK ON THE DOOR. Knock on forehead, pull hair, lift eyelid, pull nose – and on "roll out the red carpet" the child puts out his tongue. As above. Cf. Brown I, 190; Opie: *Lore*, 103; Sutton-Smith, 133; Withers, 110; Wood: *Fun*, 101.

186. THESE ARE MOTHER'S KNIVES AND FORKS. Hands are placed back to back, interlaced, fingers pointing up for knives and forks; with fingers still interlaced, hands are turned over with the backs of fingers forming table. The two little fingers are raised for the looking-glass, and the index fingers as well to re-present the cradle. As above. Cf. Baring-Gould, 241; Brown I, 184; Opie: *Dictionary*, 262; Withers, 107; Wood: *Mother Goose*, 108.

187. PUT YOUR FINGER IN THE CROW'S NEST. Child is invited to put finger in hole formed by crossing first two fingers of each hand. At "Fox came in the back door," the child's finger is pinched. As above. Cf. Brown I, 184; Opie: *Dictionary*, 175.

188. TWO LITTLE DICKIE BIRDS. Two forefingers with bits of paper stuck to the tips are placed on edge of table. Raise and lower fingers as suggested by words. Also used as a skipping rhyme. D. C. McCausland, 1963 (Grimsby, 1940s). Cf. Baring-Gould, 237; Brown I, 185; Opie: *Dictionary*, 147.

189. LITTLE PETER RABBIT. Act out italicized words by indicating ears, moving arms in flying motion, touching ear, and flicking fly away. With each repetition, one more word is omitted, being represented by the motion. As above.

190. INKY PINKY 'PIDER. One hand representing spider climbs up and down opposite arm as suggested by words. Mrs. Nancy Takerer, 1964 (Kingston, 1940s). Cf. Emrich, 109; Ritchie, 109.

191. SIX LITTLE DUCKS. Fingers represent ducks walking along to water, and then wave at top of head to represent feathers. As above.

192. I'M A LITTLE TEAPOT. One arm bent with hand on hip for handle; the other stretched out for a spout. Reverse arms for second verse. Lynn Fowke, 1963 (Saskatoon, 1950s). Cf. Wood: *Fun*, 104.

Counting Out Rhymes

These are used to determine who is "It" in various games — usually the child at whom the counter points on the last word. Sometimes the rhyme is repeated until all but one are eliminated; the remaining one then is "It". Many of these rhymes are also used for skipping.

193. ONE, TWO, THREE, FOUR. *Globe*, November 13, 1909 (Toronto). Cf. Bolton, 93; Botkin: *Treasury*, 773; Brown I, 165; Evans, 95; Newell, 201; Opie: *Dictionary*, 334; Ritchie, 13.

194. ONE, TWO, THREE, FOUR, FIVE. Stella Roode, 1961 (Montreal, 1940s). Cf. Baring-Gould, 249; Bolton, 93; Botkin: *Treasury*, 773; Douglas, 34; Emrich, 116; Opie: *Dictionary*, 344-5; Withers, 86; Wood: *Fun*, 109.

195. TWO, FOUR, SIX, EIGHT. Sackville School, 1964. Cf. Bolton, 93; Emrich, 135; Schwartz, FC 7003; Withers, 61.

196. ONE, TWO, THREE, FOUR, FIVE, SIX, SEVEN. Mrs. Smaller, from Downsview children, 1962. Cf. Baring-Gould, 249; Bolton, 94; Brown I, 165; Emrich, 121; Evans, 90; MacColl, FW 8501; Newell, 202; Sutton-Smith, 64.

197. MY FATHER HAD AN OLD HORSESHOE. Mrs. Robertson, collected in Shelburne, N.S., 1910. Cf. Bolton, 116.

198. ONE POTATO, TWO POTATO. Child counting places his fist over fists of other children in turn. East York children, 1959 (FO 259). Cf. Emrich, 121; Evans, 104; Holbrook, 123; Sutton-Smith, 68; Withers, 84.

199. BUBBLE GUM. Action as in "One Potato." Also used for skipping. Mary Jane Webb, Don Mills, Ontario, 1963.

200. INKY, PINKY, PONKY. St. Clair West School, 1964. Cf. Brown I, 166; Wood: *Mother Goose*, 83; Sutton-Smith, 64.

201. ESKIMO, ESKIMO. Each child turns around and raises his arms as he is counted out until only one is left. Mrs. Smaller, from Ted Gilson, Downsview, 1964.

202. SKY BLUE, SKY BLUE. Mrs. Smaller, from Wendy Morrow, Downsview, 1964.

203. BOY SCOUT, WATCH OUT. Child counting touches feet of other children, eliminating one foot each time, and continues until all but one have been eliminated. Mary Jane Webb, Don Mills, 1963.

204. ITTLE, OTTLE. Mrs. Robertson, collected in Shelburne, N.S., 1900s. Cf. Opie: *Dictionary*, 248; Ritchie, 14; Sutton-Smith, 63.

205. ENGINE, ENGINE, NUMBER NINE. A. Mrs. Smaller, 1962 (Owen Sound, c. 1915). B. *Globe*, November 20, 1909 (Perth, Ontario). C. Rosedale School, 1964. Cf. Bolton, 111; Botkin: *Treasury*, 768; Brown I, 168; Emrich, 120; Evans, 96; Wood: *Fun*, 53; Worstell, 36.

206. INK, MINK, WHO STINKS? A. Mrs. Robertson, collected in Shelburne, N.S., 1920s. B. Mrs. Smaller, from Rosemary Ricker, 1964. Cf. Bolton, 111; Opie: *Lore*, 48.

207. EENY MEENY MACKER RACKER. Mrs. Smaller, from William Baker, Downsview, 1964. Cf. Bolton, 104-5.

208. EENY, MEENY MINY MO. A. Claire Pratt, 1964 (Toronto, 1920s). B. Louch children, Willowdale, 1963. Cf. Bolton, 105-6; Emrich, 122; Evans, 89; Opie: *Dictionary*, 156.

209. PIGGY ON THE RAILWAY. Alice Kane, from Toronto children, 1964. Cf. Botkin: *Treasury*, 798; Douglas, 30; Hamilton, TLP 1034; Holbrook, 56; MacColl, FW 8501; Sutton-Smith, 65.

210. MISS DEFOE. *Globe*, November 20, 1909 (Perth). Cf. "Cowboy Joe."

211. EENY MEENY HIPPORY DICK. A. Phyllis M. E. Stephenson, Prescott, Ontario, from father. B. Mrs. Robertson, collected in Shelburne, N.S. (Clark's Harbour, 1910). C. Stella Roode, 1961 (Montreal, 1940s). Cf. Bolton, 107; Botkin: *Treasury*, 800; Brown I, 168.

212. GRANDFATHER HAD SOME WHEAT AND RYE. Mrs. Robertson, collected in Shelburne, 1910.

213. ONERY TWOERY ICKERY ANN. Mrs. Smaller, from Mr. Huntsman (Tintern, Ontario, c. 1900). Cf. Bolton, 94-5; Brown I, 163; Emrich, 118; Evans, 99; Newell, 197; Opie: *Dictionary*, 335-6; Wood: *Mother Goose*, 97.

214. ONERY TWOERY DICKERY DEE. *Globe*, November 20, 1909 (Perth). Cf. Baring-Gould, 249; Bolton, 97; Emrich, 119; Newell, 198; Opie: *Dictionary*, 336.

215. WIRE, BRIER, LIMBERLOCK. Sam Campsall, 1957 (Kirkland Lake, Ontario 1920s). Cf. Bolton, 102-3; Botkin; *Treasury*, 773, 787; Brown I, 160; Emrich, 116; Evans, 88; Newell, 200; Opie: *Dictionary*, 224; Wood: *Mother Goose*, 57.

216. EALY MEALY DIBBLY DICK. Sam Campsall, 1957 (Kirkland Lake, 1920s). Cf. Bolton, 107.

217. MONKEY, MONKEY. *Globe*, December 11, 1909 (Brantford, Ontario). Cf. Bolton, 112; 116; Botkin: *Treasury*, 773; Brown I, 164; Emrich, 112; Newell, 202; Wood: *Fun*, 88.

218. WHEN I WENT UP AN APPLE TREE. Mrs. Smaller, from Dr. Huntsman (Tintern, Ontario, c. 1900). Cf. Bolton, 113; Botkin: *Treasury*, 777; Emrich, 122, Hamilton, TLP 1034.

Starting Rhymes

These are used as the signal for a race or the beginning of a hide-and-seek or tag game.

219. ONE FOR THE MONEY. Mrs. Smaller, 1963 (Owen Sound, c. 1915). Cf. Baring-Gould, 259; Bolton, 119; Botkin: *Treasury*, 778; Brown I, 170; Emrich, 116; Newell, 133; Opie: *Dictionary*, 333; Sutton-Smith, 75; Withers, 42; Wood: *Mother Goose*, 96.

220. ONE TO BE READY. Alice Kane, from Toronto children, 1964. Cf. Bolton, 119; Opie: *Dictionary*, 332.

221. ONE, TWO, THREE. Mrs. Smaller, 1963 (Owen Sound, c. 1915). Cf. Bolton, 93; Botkin: *Treasury*, 780; Brown I, 166.

222. CHARLEY ON THE WATER. Formerly a ring game. Now used for tag. Louch children, Willowdale, 1963. Cf. Courlander, FC 7004; Newell, 171.

223. READY OR NOT. Mrs. Mary Jane Young, 1963 (Owen Sound, 1930s).

Taunts and Teases

224. GEORGIE PORGIE. St. Clair West School, 1964. Cf. Emrich, 109; Opie: *Dictionary*, 185.

225. TATTLE TALE, GINGER ALE. Rosedale School, 1964.

226. LIAR, LIAR. Rosedale School, 1964. Cf. Evans, 132.

227. STANDING ON THE CORNER. Sometimes used for skipping. East York children, 1959. Cf. Botkin: *Treasury*, 791; Evans, 40; Worstell, 12.

228. THERE SHE GOES. Sheila Luscombe, 1959 (FO 230). Cf. Opie: *Lore*, 182; Ritchie, 112.

229. MY FATHER IS A KING. Stella Roode, 1961 (Montreal, 1940s). Cf. Opie: *Lore*, 175.

230. TATTLE TALE TIT. East York children, 1959 (FO 273). Cf. Baring-Gould, 36; Brown I, 176; Emrich, 111; MacColl, FW 8501; Opie: *Lore*, 189; Sutton-Smith, 93.

231. THERE LIVED A GIRL. Vivienne Stenson, 1958 (Wales, 1930s). Cf. Opie: *Lore*, 175; Wood: *Mother Goose*, 88.

232. LITTLE TOMMY TINKER. Mrs. Smaller, 1963 (Owen Sound, 1920s).

233. CRY, BABY, CRY. Heard in Saskatchewan in 1920s. Cf. Baring-Gould, 310; Brown I, 176; Emrich, 110; Evans, 136; Opie: *Lore*, 188; Sutton-Smith, 93; Withers, 120; Wood: *Mother Goose*, 28.

234. KINDERGARTEN BABY. Mrs. Mary Jane Young, 1963 (Owen Sound, 1940s). Cf. Evans, 134.

235. TEETER TOTTER. As above. Cf. Opie: *Lore*, 345.

236. UP THE MOUNTAIN. Alice Kane, from Toronto children, 1963. Cf. Botkin: *Treasury*, 788.

237. I'M THE KING OF THE CASTLE. Sheila Luscombe, 1957. Cf. Baring-Gould, 82; Daiken, 12; Gomme I, 300; Hamilton, TLP 1034; Opie: *Dictionary*, 254.

238. CALL ME THIS, CALL ME THAT. Alice Kane, from Toronto children, 1962.

239. STICKS AND STONES. Rosedale School, 1964. Cf. Emrich, 111; Evans, 131; Opie: *Dictionary*, 403; *Lore*, 160; Sutton-Smith, 93; Withers, 128.

240. ROSY'S IT. St. Clair West School, 1964. Cf. Botkin: *Treasury*, 769; Emrich, 110; Evans, 136.

241. COWARDY, COWARDY, CUSTARD. Heard in Saskatchewan in 1920s. Cf. Baring-Gould, 310; Evans, 136; Opie: *Lore*, 185; Withers, 120.

242. FATTY, FATTY. Mrs. Smaller, from Downsview children, 1962. Cf. Emrich, 109; Evans, 142.

243. BLUE-EYED BEAUTY. Edith Ferguson, 1963 (St. Elmo, c. 1915). Cf. Brown I, 175; Evans, 143; Opie: *Lore*, 327; Withers, 174.

244. JOHNNY ON THE WOODPILE. Alice Kane, 1963, from Toronto children. Cf. Brown I, 177; Withers, 44.

245. I SAW YOU IN THE ORCHARD. Mrs. Smaller, from Downsview children, 1962. Cf. Evans, 145.

246. ANNE, ANNE, IF YOU'RE ABLE. Mrs. Smaller, from Rosemary Ricker, 1964. Cf. *Southern Folklore Quarterly* XXVII (1963), 207.

247. MARY JANE IS NO GOOD. Alice Kane, 1963 (St. John, N.B., 1920s). Cf. Emrich, 111; Opie: *Lore*, 176.

248. POLLY'S MAD. Alice Kane, 1963, from girl who learned it in Alberta. Cf. Brown I, 175; Emrich, 110; Evans, 144; Withers, 123.

249. ROSES ARE RED. Mrs. Smaller, from Downsview children, 1961. Cf. Evans, 138, 142; Opie: *Lore*, 171.

250. BILL THE RILL. Other names were used in a similar pattern. Mrs. Mary Jane Young, 1963 (Owen Sound, 1940s). Cf. Brown I, 178; Opie: *Lore*, 158, Withers, 117.

251. ORDER IN THE COURT-HOUSE. Heard in Saskatchewan, 1920s. Cf. Opie: *Lore*, 194.

Tricks and Treats

252. PETER AND PAUL AND PINCH ME. Also used as "Adam and Eve and Pinch Me." Louch children, Willowdale, 1963. Cf. Baring-Gould, 251; Botkin: *Treasury*, 782; Emrich, 162; Evans, 140; Opie: *Lore*, 59; Withers, 11; Wood: *Mother Goose*, 92.

253. ICE CREAM AND JELLY. Alice Kane, from Toronto children, 1962. Cf. Botkin: *Treasury*, 769.

254. HERE COMES A BUMBLE-BEE. Eleanor Kelly, 1964 (learned in 1920s from father who came from Guelph).

255. MY AUNT JANE. Alice Kane, 1963 (Belfast, c. 1915).

256. HIPPITY HOP TO THE BARBER SHOP. Alice Kane, 1963, from Toronto children. Cf. Emrich, 108; Opie: *Dictionary*, 232; Wood: *Mother Goose*, 43.

257. WATERMELONS. Derived from a blackface minstrel song. D. C. McCausland, 1963 (Grimsby, 1940s). Cf. Brown III, 540-1.

258. OPEN YOUR MOUTH. Heard in Saskatchewan in 1920s. Cf. Brown I, 202.

259. FISHY, FISHY. Eleanor Kelly, 1964 (learned in 1920s from father who came from Guelph). Cf. Baring-Gould, 326; Botkin: *Treasury*, 784; Wood: *Mother Goose*, 5.

260. WHEN YOU PASS THE PINK ICE CREAM. Alice Kane, 1963, from Toronto children.

Strange Stories

261. I'LL TELL YOU A STORY. A. Frank Fowke, 1963 (Saskatchewan, c. 1915). B. Mrs. Mary Jane Young, 1963 (Owen Sound, 1930s). Cf. Botkin: *Treasury*, 786-7; Emrich, 105; Opie: *Dictionary*, 233.

262. NEBUCHADNEZZAR. Alice Kane, from Toronto children, 1962. Cf. Brown I, 314; Sutton-Smith, 95; Wood: *Mother Goose*, 53.

263. FUZZY WUZZY. Holy Name School, 1964.

264. AWAY DOWN SOUTH. Bruce School, 1962. Cf. Evans, 20, Withers, 5.

265. THERE WAS A LITTLE MAN. Doris Mosdell, 1963 (first verse from mother who came from Guelph, Ontario; second verse from grandmother who came from Newfoundland, c. 1925). Cf. Botkin: *Treasury*, 781; Hamilton, TLP 1034; Opie: *Dictionary*, 289.

266. JOHN HAD SOME CAKE. Alice Kane, from Toronto children, 1962. Cf. Opie: *Lore*, 97.

267. ROBERT AND BOBBIT. A. Mrs. Robertson, from friend in Shelburne, N.S., who learned it c. 1910. B. Boy in Bruce School, 1962. Cf. Baring-Gould, 33, 34; Opie: *Dictionary*, 372-3.

268. THIS IS THE DAY. Margaret Berry, from Toronto children, 1962. Cf. Record, Prestige/International 13025.

269. IF I WERE A CASSOWARY. *Globe*, December 11, 1909 (Brantford, Ontario). Cf. Ritchie, 112.

270. A FLY AND A FLEA. Mrs. Robertson, from friend in Shelburne, N.S., who learned it c. 1910. Cf. Justus, 14.

271. IT WAS MIDNIGHT. Alice Kane, from Toronto children, 1962. Cf. Randolph III, 204; Withers, 187.

272. LADIES AND JELLYPOTS. Margaret Bagshaw, from her niece, 1963. Cf. Opie: *Lore*, 25.

273. AS I WENT UP THE HOOMP-ME-SHOOMP. Mrs. Robertson, from friend in Shelburne, N.S. Cf. Wood: *Fun*, 103.

274. A HORSE AND A FLEA. Bruce School, 1962. Cf. Withers, 37.

Silly Songs

275. ROLL OVER. Catharine Potts and Judy Crawford, 1960. Cf. Opie: *Lore*, 31; Ritchie, 109.

276. I WENT TO TOLEDO. Mrs. Smaller, 1963 (Owen Sound, 1930s). Cf. Withers, 186.

277. MOUSIE, MOUSIE. Mrs. Goldenberg, 1962 (Scotland, 1930s).

278. THE BABY PRUNE. Secord School, 1960 (FO 308).

279. THE FROG IN THE BOG. Mrs. Smaller, 1963 (Owen Sound, c. 1932).

280. YON YONSON. Lynn Fowke, 1963 (Saskatchewan, 1950s). Cf. Record, Columbia ML 5339.

281. THE BUMBLE-BEE. Mrs. Nancy Takerer, from son Derek, 1967.

282. I'M A NUT. Mrs. Nancy Takerer, 1963 (Saskatchewan, 1950s). Cf. Withers, 185.

283. THE LITTLE SKUNK. Mrs. Nancy Takerer, 1963 (Kingston, 1940s).

284. FOUND A PEANUT. Louch children, Willowdale, 1963.

285. BANANA BIRD. Mrs. Harvey Louch, Willowdale, 1963 (Toronto, 1920s).

286. A LOAD OF NAILS. Mrs. Webb, from Dr. Spicer/Sterling, Maynard, Ontario, 1964 (learned c. 1910).

287. OLD AUNT MARIAR. Mrs. Louch, Willowdale, 1963 (Toronto, 1920s). Cf. Brown I, 199.

288. DO YOUR EARS HANG LOW? Usually sung in a less innocent version. Bruce School, 1962.

289. I DON'T WANT NO MORE OF ARMY LIFE. Louch children, Willowdale, 1963. Cf. Ritchie, 40-1.

290. I GAVE HER KISSES ONE. Mrs. Ethel Minifie, Peterborough, Ontario, 1957 (Frankford, Ontario, c. 1910), (Prestige/International 25014). Cf. Brown III, 368-9; Randolph III, 89-91.

291. I WITH I WATH A FITH. Mrs. Smaller, 1962 (Owen Sound, 1920s).

292. MY BODY LIES OVER THE OCEAN. Bruce School, 1962.

293. BYE, BYE, LONGJOHNS. Louch children, Willowdale, 1963.

294. BUY ME A BROOM. Mrs. Webb, from William Barkeley, Merrickville, Ontario, 1964 (learned c. 1900).

295. THREE KINGS, Alice Kane, from Toronto children, 1962. Cf. Opie: *Lore*, 88.

296. WHILE SHEPHERDS WASHED THEIR SOCKS. As above. Cf. Opie: *Lore*, 88.

297. HELEN HAD A STEAMBOAT. Bruce School, 1962. Cf. Opie: *Lore*, 94.

298. CHEER, BOYS, CHEER. Rosedale School, 1964.

299. THE BURNING OF THE SCHOOL. As above. Cf. Opie: *Lore*, 374.

300. I LOVE LITTLE WILLIE. Mrs. Geraldine Sullivan, Lakefield, Ontario, 1957 (Peterborough, 1930s), (Folkways FM 4005). Cf. Brown III, 361-3; Randolph III, 98-100.

Bibliography

Baring-Gould, William S. and Ceil. *The Annotated Mother Goose*. New York: Clarkson N. Potter, 1962.

Bolton, Henry C. *The Counting Out Rhymes of Children*. London: Elliott Stack, 1888.

Botkin, B. A. *The American Play-Party Song*. New York: Frederick Ungar, 1937; reprinted 1963.

Botkin, B. A. *A Treasury of American Folklore*. New York: Crown Publishers, 1954.

Brown. *The Frank C. Brown Collection of North Carolina Folklore*. Vols. I and III. Durham: Duke University Press, 1952.

Courlander, Harold. *Ring Games*. Folkways Record FC 7004, New York, 1953.

Daiken, Leslie. *Children's Games Throughout the Year*. New York and London: B. T. Batsford, 1949.

Douglas, Norman. *London Street Games*. London: Chatto and Windus, 1931.

Emrich, Marion Vallat and George Korson. *The Child's Book of Folklore*. New York: Dial Press, 1947.

Evans, Patricia. *Rimbles*. New York: Doubleday, 1961.

Gomme, Alice B. *The Traditional Games of England, Scotland, and Ireland*. 2 vols. London: David Nutt, 1894, 1898. Reprinted New York: Dover, 1964.

Hamilton, Diane. *Early in the Morning*. Tradition Record, TLP 1034.

Holbrook, David. *Children's Games*. London: Gordon Fraser, 1957.

Justus, May. *The Complete Peddler's Pack*. Knoxville: University of Tennessee Press, 1957.

MacColl, Ewan and Dominic Behan. *The Singing Streets*. Folkways Record FW 3562, New York, 1958.

Newell, William W. *Games and Songs of American Children*. New York: Harper & Bros, 1903. Reprinted New York: Dover, 1963.

Opie, Iona and Peter. *The Lore and Language of Schoolchildren*. London: Oxford University Press, 1959.

Opie, Iona and Peter. *The Oxford Dictionary of Nursery Rhymes*. London: Oxford University Press, 1951 .

Randolph, Vance, and Floyd C. Shoemaker. *Ozark Folksongs*. 4 vols. Columbia: The State Historical Society of Missouri, 1946-1950.

Ritchie, James. T. R. *The Singing Street*. Edinburgh and London: Oliver & Boyd, 1964.

Schwartz, Tony. *One, Two, Three and a Zing Zing Zing*. Folkways Record FC 7003, New York, 1953.

Seeger, Pete. *Jump Rope*. Folkways Record FC 7029. New York, 1953.

Sutton-Smith, Brian. *The Games of New Zealand Children*. Berkeley and Los Angeles: University of California Press, 1959.

Withers, Carl. *A Rocket in my Pocket*. New York: Holt, Rinehart and Winston, 1948.

Wood, Ray. *The American Mother Goose*. Philadelphia and New York: J. P. Lippincott, 1938.

Wood, Ray. *Fun in American Folk Rhymes*. Philadelphia and New York: J. P. Lippincott, 1952.

Worstell, Emma Victor. *Jump the Rope Jingles*. New York: Macmillan, 1961.

THE TYPE-FACE CHOSEN FOR THIS BOOK IS PALATINO, SET IN CANADA BY COOPER & BEATTY, LIMITED.
THE BOOK WAS PRINTED IN ITALY BY ARNOLDO MONDADORI, OFFICINE GRAFICHE.